'I won't . . . slee

His smile was hard
you wide awake.'

'You know what I'm talking about.' Caryn's voice was ragged. 'You can joke about it all you like, but I'm serious!'

'Who's joking?' He was looking at her now as if he were seeing her for the first time—and not particularly liking what he saw.

Dear Reader

The nights are drawing in again . . . the perfect excuse for
snuggling up with a Mills & Boon romance! November is
the time for bonfires and fireworks, of course—and
you'll find plenty of sparks flying between the heroes and
heroines in this month's collection of love stories! Look
out for books by some of your favourite authors . . . and,
if you're missing the summer sun, why not let us
transport you to sunny California and exotic Mexico? So
shut out the winter darkness, and enter the warm and
wonderful world of Mills & Boon!

The Editor

Kay Thorpe was born in Sheffield in 1935. She tried out
a variety of jobs after leaving school. Writing began as a
hobby, becoming a way of life only after she had her first
completed novel accepted for publication in 1968. Since
then, she's written over fifty and lives now with her
husband, son, German shepherd dog and lucky black cat
on the outskirts of Chesterfield in Derbyshire. Her
interests include reading, hiking, and travel.

Recent titles by the same author:

A RECKLESS ATTRACTION

WORLDS
APART

BY
KAY THORPE

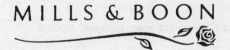

MILLS & BOON

MILLS & BOON LIMITED
ETON HOUSE, 18-24 PARADISE ROAD
RICHMOND, SURREY TW9 1SR

*MILLS & BOON and the Rose Device
are trademarks of the publisher.*

*First published in Great Britain 1994
by Mills & Boon Limited*

© Kay Thorpe 1994

*Australian copyright 1994   Philippine copyright 1994
This edition 1994*

ISBN 0 263 78745 1

*Set in Times Roman 10 on 12 pt.
01-9411-54240 C*

Made and printed in Great Britain

CHAPTER ONE

THE sea was way out at present, the evening tide not due to turn for another hour or so, although when it did it came in fast.

Caryn headed away from the town, carrying her shoes in her hand in order to feel the sand gritting between her toes. Living on the coast was one of life's compensations as far as she was concerned. She always felt sorry for those who only saw the sea infrequently.

As always when she came down here at this time of day, this time of year, memory came flooding back full-force. She wasn't sure why she continued to do it—unless it was to keep the hatred alive in her heart. At sixteen she hadn't known what it was to hate, until Logan Bannister had taught her. Even after two years, the hurt of it could still constrict her throat.

Lost in the past, she neither saw nor heard the horse approaching, only becoming aware when it was almost on her. She stood rooted to the spot as the man astride the big chestnut brought it to a halt in front of her, gazing up at him in disbelief. Her mind was playing tricks on her; it had to be!

Steely grey eyes slid over her, taking in every detail of her piquant features under the heavy crop of blonde hair before moving on down to linger for a lengthy moment on the jut of her firm young breasts beneath the thin cotton of her shirt. A muscle jerked faintly in the well-defined jawline.

'Hello, Caryn,' he said, coming back to her face. 'You've grown up.'

'It happens to us all,' she responded with an effort, fighting the shock. 'Some faster than others.'

The muscle jerked again, and his hands tightened momentarily on the reins. His smile was brief and wry. 'You've also acquired a sharp tongue.'

'Only where I consider it merited.' Caryn was surprised by her own turn of phrase. She drew herself up to her full five feet four and slid her hands into her jeans pockets, unaware of how the movement emphasised the slender curve of her hips. 'How long are you home for?'

One dark brow lifted. 'Is it important to you?'

'Not to me,' she claimed, 'but it may be to Margot.'

'I hardly think so. She married Duncan Ashley.'

'On the rebound. After you ran out on her!'

Sensing the animosity simmering in the air, the chestnut made a restless movement, brought under control by the firmness of the hands holding the rein. Logan Bannister slid a leg over the animal's back and dropped lithely to the ground, tall and leanly muscled in the tailored breeches and fine white shirt. His shoulders were broad and powerful, his forearms tanned the colour of old teak beneath their light coating of dark hair. His face was tanned too, skin stretched taut over hard male cheekbones. Looking up at him from her eight or more inches disadvantage, Caryn felt every nerve in her body tense anew.

'One thing we should have clear,' he said softly. 'I never at any time gave Margot grounds to believe we had a future together. If she thought otherwise, then I'm afraid she was mistaken.'

Blue eyes flashed. 'You mean she was just one more scalp to your belt!'

Anger flared in the grey eyes and just as abruptly faded, replaced by a weary acceptance. 'You don't have to remind me. I've lived with it this last two years.'

'You think I haven't?' This time there was no attempt at concealment. 'For all you knew—or cared—I might have been pregnant!'

'If you had been I would have heard about it,' he said.

'And done what?' she demanded. 'Come back and married me?'

His lips twisted. 'I'd have faced whatever music I was called on to face, but I doubt if marriage would have been seen as the ideal solution by anyone at the time.'

Caryn drew in an unsteady breath. He was so much in control of the situation, so utterly unrepentant. When she found her voice again there was venom in it. 'There are no circumstances in which *I* would have considered marrying a rapist!'

'Rapist?' The tone was ironic. 'I don't seem to recall having to use any force.'

She flushed hotly, only too well aware that the word had been ill-chosen. 'Seducer, then,' she substituted, rallying her forces with an effort.

'But from which side did the seduction come?' The question was dangerously soft and silky. 'You were so eager for my kisses, for the touch of my hands—for anything and everything I wanted to do to you. Did you make one attempt to stop me?'

'Swine!' Her voice choked off. Blinking back the hot, fierce tears, she turned blindly away.

'Caryn, wait!' He was right behind her, seizing her by the shoulder to spin her back towards him. There was regret in the grey eyes. 'I shouldn't have said that.'

'Why not?' she asked huskily. 'It's true. I threw myself at you.'

'But I didn't have to respond,' he said. 'If I'd packed you off home that night the way I should have done, it would never have happened. I was the one at fault, not you.'

She was silent, gazing up at him, conscious of the burning warmth of his fingers reaching through to her skin—those same fingers that had once caressed her with such tender passion; her breasts tingled at the very memory of it. He aroused the same feelings in her now as then, she acknowledged, distressing though it was to admit it. Only it made no difference to her hatred of him.

'Let go of me!' she said through her teeth. 'I can't bear you to touch me!'

He did so immediately, standing back with hands raised in a gesture of defence, expression wry. 'All right, then, I won't. Just listen to what I have to say.'

'There's nothing *to* say,' she fired back at him. 'Nothing I'd want to hear—unless it's to tell me you'll be leaving again tomorrow.'

Logan was silent for a long moment, studying her face, his own blanked now of all expression. 'I'm afraid I can't do that,' he said at length.

'Then if not tomorrow, when?'

It was another moment or two before he answered, still giving little of his thoughts and feelings away. 'I'm home for good—or at least for the foreseeable future.'

Caryn felt her heart give a painful lurch before settling back down to a steady if somewhat faster beat. 'I thought you had business interests overseas,' she got out at last.

'So I have,' he acknowledged. 'And still shall have. My partner will continue to run the stud farm in Australia, while I take over here.'

'I'd have thought,' she said, 'that the time to do that would have been after your father died last year. Assuming, of course,' she added pointedly, 'that you weren't actually disinherited.'

Broad shoulders lifted. 'Let's just say there was a condition I wasn't prepared to fulfil at the time.'

'But now you are?'

'Now I must.' He paused, eyes reflective as they dwelt on her face. 'My mother has less than a year to live. I intend to see she has everything she wants—whatever the cost. She wants me here, so I stay. I'm sorry if that doesn't meet with your approval, but I really don't have any other choice.'

Caryn bit her lip. There was no way she could oppose that statement. Logan was home, and she would simply have to grin and bear it.

'I'm sorry,' she said. 'About your mother, I mean. Can nothing be done?'

He shook his head. 'Nothing that hasn't already been tried. It's a form of leukaemia, arrestable for a time but incurable in the long term. It's all downhill from here.'

'She knows the prognosis?'

'Of course. She insisted on it.' His smile was brief. 'She was always the brave one.'

Caryn knew the woman only by sight. The Bannisters moved in a different social circle. If Margot Sinclair's younger brother hadn't invited her to that party two years ago, she would probably never have met Logan either.

'I'm sorry,' she said again. 'I really am. It must be dreadful to know you're going to die.' She hesitated, searching for some way of extricating herself from this whole situation with a degree of dignity. 'I'd better be getting back,' was all she could come up with. 'Mom will be wondering where I got to.'

'How are your parents?' Logan asked as she began turning away, and she looked back at him with reluctance.

'They're fine.'

'Good.' For a brief moment he seemed to hesitate, as if about to say something else, then he shook his head and swung himself back up into the saddle, holding the animal on the spot for a moment to lift a hand in a brief salute.

Caryn stood gazing after him as he cantered off in the direction from which he had come. It was still there. Just the same. Hatred was no barrier, it seemed, against physical attraction. She could remember as if it were yesterday that heart-jerking moment when she had looked up into those grey eyes for the very first time.

At sixteen, her emotions had been so intense, so immediate, so indiscriminate, his fifteen years' seniority no obstacle. To Logan neither, it had turned out, but only up to a point.

With Whitegates only a couple of miles up the coast, and Barston the nearest town, there was little doubt that she would be seeing him around in the weeks and months to come, disturbing though that fact might be. She would simply have to learn to live with it.

Home was no more than a ten-minute walk from the beach in a suburb that had once been a village in its own right before earlier prosperity had spread Barston out to encompass it. It had been a very wet May and early June this year, giving no boost at all to the holiday trade on which the town depended. One of the few unspoiled coastal townships left in England, boasted the seasonal brochure with some truth, but that very lack of modernisation made the weather all the more vital to its viability as a resort.

Detached from its neighbours, and built to a cottagey style that blended well with the general Norfolk landscape, the house had been in the Gregory family for three generations. In today's financial climate, maintenance had lapsed a little, lending the place a slightly shabby appearance due to peeling paintwork. Caryn's father was no handyman, and he knew it, preferring to hire professionals as and when he could afford it. Caryn had offered to try her hand at the job, but he wouldn't hear of it. No daughter of his, he said, was to go climbing ladders on his behalf.

Indoors, she followed the aroma of newly baked bread to the comfortable family kitchen, smiling at the woman washing up pans at the sink.

'That smells good! Thank heaven for an old-fashioned mother!'

Susan Gregory laughed, pushing back a straying lock of fair hair with a soapy hand. 'If liking to bake is old-fashioned, then that's what I am. It wouldn't do you any harm to learn.'

'My hand would never be as light as yours,' Caryn disclaimed. 'It's more used to hammering on a typewriter. One of these days, Taylor, Taylor and Simmerson might step into the twentieth century and acquire a word-processor. It would certainly make life easier.'

'Why don't you suggest it?' asked her mother, and received a wry shrug.

'I have, but the words fell on deaf ears. We "have no need of new-fangled notions", to quote Mr Taylor senior. I don't suppose they have while they can find someone mad enough to tackle the job as it stands.'

'They pay you well,' Susan responded on a faintly reproving note. 'You're not thinking of looking for another job, are you?'

'In Barston?' It was Caryn's turn to laugh. 'I'd be lucky to find one that wasn't seasonal. Short of moving elsewhere, which I've no intention of doing, I suppose I must count my blessings.'

'If you'd done as well in school as everyone expected you to do, and stayed on to take your A levels, you'd have had far more scope,' her mother pointed out, not for the first time. 'I could never understand why you finished up with such low marks in most of your GCSE subjects.'

'Exam nerves, I expect,' claimed Caryn with a lightness she was far from feeling. 'Anyway, I did well enough in business college, even if the prospects round here are somewhat limited.' She went to pick up the kettle, anxious for a change of subject. 'I'll make some tea. Dad's always ready for a cup about this time.'

Her father was seated reading the evening newspaper when she took the tray through some minutes later.

'Not going out tonight?' he asked mildly, taking the cup she poured for him from her.

'I've been out,' she said.

'To the beach?' He shook his head. 'That's no way to spend Saturday evening. At least, it wasn't in my younger days. You spend too much time on your own, Caryn. A pretty girl like you can't be short of companionship.'

'None I'm particularly interested in.' Caryn kept her tone deliberately light. 'Don't worry about it, Dad. I like being on my own. Anyway, Jane will be back from holiday next week, so I shan't be much longer. Unless she decides to get serious over Roy Gillingham, of course, in which case girlfriends have to take a back seat.'

'She's too young to be serious about anyone,' John Gregory 'eclared. 'So is Roy Gillingham, if it comes to that. Your mother and I were both in our middle twenties before we married, which is why we've lasted so well. No teenagers can know their own minds.'

'Probably not,' Caryn murmured, steeling herself against the intruding memories. 'I think I'll have an early night and catch up on some reading. Mom said she'll be through in a minute.'

Redecorated by herself only a few weeks ago in green and white with touches of pink in the curtains and covers, her bedroom somehow no longer pleased her as much. Lying on her back on the bed, gazing at the ceiling, she felt confined and restless. There had to be more to life than this day-to-day existence. Perhaps it was time, after all, that she thought about moving away from Barston. Not just to Norwich either, but further afield. There was a whole world out there waiting to be explored.

It was seeing Logan again that had brought this on, she knew. Closing her eyes, she could visualise him in detail. Remembering was painful, but she couldn't stop herself from doing it . . .

'And this is Michael's little friend, Caryn,' declared Margot Sinclair on an indulgent note.

Logan Bannister's smile was slow, eyes riveting as he extended a hand. 'Hello, Caryn.'

'Hello.' Her voice sounded odd, Caryn thought, hoping the warmth she could feel under her skin didn't show in her face. She wasn't normally prone to blushing, but then neither was she normally prone to falling in love at a moment's notice. Logan was devastating; there was no other word for it! Not handsome in the way of her favourite film star, perhaps, yet somehow infinitely more exciting.

The fingers which had closed about hers were long and tensile, his grasp hinting of a latent strength. Without looking directly, she was aware of the crisp whiteness of his shirt cuff against tanned skin, of the glint of gold from the watch encircling one lean wrist. Having contact removed was sheer deprivation.

'Are you in university too?' he asked.

Margot laughed. 'Hardly, darling! Caryn's still in school. About to sit your GCSEs, I believe?' she added.

'Next month,' Caryn confirmed with reluctance; she would have been more than ready to accept a couple of years' promotion in this man's eyes.

'With straight A passes in all subjects,' said Michael Sinclair lightly, slinging a casual arm about her shoulders. 'Isn't that right, angel?'

'Hopefully,' she murmured.

'Good luck,' proffered Logan, and she felt the impact of his smile once more.

'Are he and your sister engaged or anything?' she asked Michael on what she hoped was a casual note as the older couple moved on.

'Not as yet,' came the answer. 'Although I'm pretty sure Margot has it in mind. And what she wants she usually gets.'

Caryn didn't doubt it. A sizzlingly beautiful brunette, Margot Sinclair could probably have any man she chose. Logan must be around thirty himself, and eminently eligible. The Bannisters had a stud farm a few miles along the coast, and were said to be extremely wealthy. Logan certainly looked the part. The pale grey suit he was wearing had a cut and fit unmistakable even to her relatively untutored eyes.

She had seen him before, of course, but only at a distance when riding his horse along the beach, which he seemed to do most evenings. Having met him now, there was no reason why she shouldn't wave a greeting in future, she thought. He might even stop to talk, although about what she had no idea. It didn't really matter providing she got to be near him again.

Up until now, Michael had seemed so mature and sophisticated at nineteen and in his first year at university. She had been flattered by his attention at the spring dance last month, and hadn't been reluctant to see him each weekend since, but there had never been any real romantic interest on her side. His kisses were no more than pleasant, while she imagined Logan Bannister's to be out of this world! He was a man, not a boy. A real man!

She made sure to be on the beach the following evening around six-thirty, heart leaping when she saw him coming. He reined in at once when he spotted her, smiling down at her with every indication of pleasure.

'I've seen you down here most evenings,' he said, 'but I didn't know you were Michael's girlfriend.'

'I'm not,' Caryn denied, and saw his brows lift. 'I mean we're just friends,' she amended.

'What else, at your age?' Logan asked lightly. He touched his heels to the stallion's sides, lifting a hand in farewell. 'Bye for now.'

That was the beginning. Before too long he was not only stopping to talk to her, but getting down from his horse to walk with her while they talked about everything under the sun. Caryn lived for those moments. Unlike her parents, Logan treated her as an adult. With him she felt like an adult—a grown woman. Certainly the emotions he aroused in her went far beyond a girlish crush.

The suspicion that he might return her feelings came to her gradually, sparked by a certain look in his eyes, a certain note in his voice. Margot Sinclair might have it in sheer looks, but could she hold his interest in quite the same way with her views on current affairs, on literature and art? Could she make him laugh with her comments the way little Caryn Gregory did?

Because of Logan, she found herself reading *Romeo and Juliet*, which she was studying for GCSE, with new insight, identifying with the lovelorn teenager in a way she had never done before. But it was in *Antony and Cleopatra* that she found the real stimulation of her awakening senses. Here was a woman whose love for a man knew no bounds—a woman who saw no shame in declaring that love both in words and in action—a woman for whom there could never be any other man but Antony.

For Caryn there could never be any other man but Logan. She already knew that for a fact.

With her mind constantly in the clouds, her GCSEs were a disaster. Apart from English Literature, she doubted if she would finish up with more than Cs or even Ds for the rest. But it was a long time before the results would be through, and at present she had far more pressing concerns. Before anything, she had to know how Logan really felt about her.

Normally she would walk to meet him along the beach. This particular evening she sat and waited for him to come to her, heart thudding against her ribcage in the knowledge of what she was about to say to him. Like Antony, he would sweep her into his arms, press kisses on her lips, her eyes—everywhere and anywhere he cared to press them!

Then he was there, reining in to sit looking down at her with an expression in his eyes that told her she wasn't mistaken.

'Take me for a ride,' she said, and he laughed, swinging her up in front of him, his breath warm on her neck, his body so hard and muscular at her back.

She had never ridden on a horse in her life before, but it felt so good to be up there above the sands, secure in Logan's embrace, oblivious of the way her short summer skirt rode up her thighs. He kept the animal to a steady walk, one hand on the rein, the other about her waist. She could feel the pressure of his thighs against the back of hers, stirring her senses to a point where she scarcely knew what she was doing any more, and cared even less.

Blood singing in her ears, she took hold of his hand and moved it upwards to the region of her left breast, hearing his sudden sharp intake of breath as his fingers came into contact with the firm young curve.

'For God's sake, Caryn!' he said gruffly against her hair. 'You don't know what you're doing!'

'Yes, I do,' she whispered. 'Don't you like touching me this way?'

'Like it?' The words came out on a groan. 'Of course I like it! I . . .' He broke off abruptly, moving the hand sharply away. 'I think I'd better put you down.'

He brought the horse to a halt and dismounted, reaching up to seize her about the waist, face grimly set. 'Come on.'

Caryn allowed herself to slide down into his arms, putting her own about his neck and burying her face in his shirt-front as she found her feet. 'Don't leave me,' she begged. 'I love you, Logan!'

His whole body was rigid. 'You don't know what you're saying,' he reiterated. 'You don't even know what love is.'

'Yes, I do. It's the way you make me feel.' She was desperate to convince him. She lifted her face to his, searching the grey eyes and seeing the look she had seen before slowly ousting the grimness. Instinctively she pressed herself closer to him, feeling the hardness of his chest against her breasts, the tingling in her nipples. Her lips were slightly parted, youthfully full and moist, trembling a little in their eagerness for his touch.

He kissed her roughly, as if in a deliberated attempt to frighten her off, but she refused to be intimidated by it, kissing him back with a fervency that took him by surprise and elicited an involuntary response. It was so different from Michael's kisses, stirring emotions only vaguely sensed up to now, turning her limbs to jelly and starting a burning heat in her lower body.

A low groan broke from Logan's lips as she moved instinctively against him, and he tried to put her from him. But she wouldn't be put, clinging to him with all her strength, wanting this to continue. For a brief moment he resisted, then he groaned again and went on kissing her, pressuring her lips apart and sending quivers of excitement racing through her. He was Antony, she was Cleopatra, and they were in love. Wonderfully, intoxicatingly in love!

When he lifted her in his arms and carried her into the sand dunes it was all part of that same scenario. When he laid her on the sand and lowered himself to her she knew nothing but delight in his masculine assertion.

Her blouse was a flimsy, sleeveless affair buttoned down the front, her brassière a wisp of lace that gave easily to the seeking hand. The touch of his fingers on her bare skin made her shiver. Such a delicate touch, tracing a spiral about her breast until it finally reached her aching nipple.

Caryn stifled a cry as he lowered his head to take the proud little nub of flesh between his lips, unable to bear the exquisite sensation yet desperate for it to continue. Her hands slid of their own accord into the crisp, clean thickness of his hair, fingers digging into his scalp, her body arched towards the marauding mouth. She had read so many literary—and not so literary—descriptions of lovemaking, but never in her wildest dreams had she imagined it to be as wonderful as this! She was on fire all the way through.

Elasticated at the waist, her skirt slid easily down over her hips. Logan followed its passage with his lips, fluttering the skin of her abdomen and causing her thigh muscles to go into sudden spasm. She caught at him frantically as he brushed the lacy edging of her briefs, hardly knowing what she wanted at that moment. He didn't resist, but lifted his head first to find her breast and then her lips again kissing her back into a state where she cared about nothing else but having this go on.

He removed her remaining undergarment with dexterity, sliding his hand back along the length of her leg to seek her innermost secrets. Eyes closed, she was lost in a world of pure sensation, pliant to his every demand. There was a brief moment when she thought he was leaving her, but then he came right over her and there was a wholly new sensation, a burgeoning pressure that parted her thighs and brought a bubbling cry to her lips.

Her eyes flew open in surprise as the pressure increased, her muscles tensing involuntarily against the intrusion. It was so much more than she had anticipated—

if she had thought this far at all—stretching her, filling her, forging a passage to the very centre of her being.

The pressure became suddenly unbearable, flaring into sharp pain that was gone as quickly as it came, to be replaced by a wonderful glowing warmth. The movement came to her easily, instinctively, lifting her hips in a rhythm as old as time. She heard the rasp of Logan's breath in her ears but was unaware that the moaning sound accompanying was coming from her own lips. There was a moment of pure ecstasy when she thought she must have died and gone straight to heaven, then everything dissolved into nothingness.

How long the two of them lay, Caryn had no clear idea. She came back to earth to find herself gazing into an evening-misted sky, aware of the weight and warmth holding her down, and of her spreadeagled lower limbs.

They were still joined as one, she realised, although the pressure had decreased to a point where the unity was more sensed than actually felt. She had done that to him, she thought exultantly. Like Cleopatra, she had given her man the ultimate pleasure of climactic fulfilment. She felt neither shame nor regret. At least not then. The wonder of it was all too devastatingly new for any opposing emotion to find purchase.

'We belong together now,' she whispered into the dark hair lying so close to her lips. 'For always!'

For a brief moment there was no response—no movement at all from the man lying with head buried in her shoulder. When he did move it was abruptly, levering himself upright without looking at her directly, face taut and alien.

Too stunned to react, Caryn felt her skirt tossed over her legs as if to hide her nudity, and then he was gone from her line of vision altogether.

When she did finally raise herself up on her elbows, Logan was sitting with his back to her a few feet away, arms resting on bent knees, head lowered. He looked, Caryn thought, like a man with a great weight on his shoulders.

'What's wrong?' she asked hesitantly, still not wholly understanding the sudden change in him.

'Get dressed,' he said without lifting his head. His voice was rough.

She did so with hands gone suddenly nerveless, fastening the tiny buttons of her blouse with difficulty. Only when she stopped moving did Logan stir himself to turn and look at her. His expression was under strict control.

'That should never have happened,' he said gruffly. 'I'm not making any excuses, because there aren't any. You're just a child, Caryn. I had no right to take that away from you.'

'I'm not a child!' She was eager to convince him of it, face lit by her turbulent inner emotions. 'I love you, Logan. You only did what I wanted you to do—what all men and women in love do!'

'You're not a woman, and you're not in love with me.' The statement was bald, the tone curt. 'Infatuated, perhaps, but that will pass. What happened just now . . .' He paused, biting his lip. 'I can only hope to God that there are no repercussions.'

'It isn't infatuation,' Caryn protested, not fully registering the latter remark. 'Do you think I don't know the difference? I *love* you, Logan! I want us to be together always!'

'It isn't possible.' He said it between gritted teeth, body taut as a bowstring. 'You're still at school, for one thing.'

'I can leave. I hate it, anyway!'

'No, you don't,' he returned. 'You're going to stay on and take your A levels, maybe go to university. You'll probably fall in love more than once before you find the man you really want to spend the rest of your life with.'

'I already found him,' she insisted, refusing to be turned from what she knew to be the truth. 'There'll never be anyone else. I only want *you*!'

The skin about the strong mouth whitened as his teeth came sharply together. 'But *I* don't want *you*,' he said. 'Not any more. I can't replace what you gave me, and I'm truly sorry about that, but it doesn't make any difference. You've your whole life ahead of you. You'll soon forget me.'

'No, I won't!' She still couldn't believe what he was telling her. Not after the way he had kissed her, caressed her, been a living part of her. He *had* to love her!

She caught at his arm as he began to rise, pulling with all her strength to restrain him. 'You can't just go. I won't let you go!'

Features set, eyes like steel, he prised her fingers away from his sleeve and got up, leaving her sitting there in the sand with realisation finally coming over her like a heavy black cloud.

'I have to go,' he said. 'I've left myself no choice. You won't see me again unless . . .' He broke off, jaw tensing, then turned away abruptly to make his way over to where the chestnut still stood patiently waiting.

Numbed throughout, Caryn watched him swing himself into the saddle and canter off without a backward glance. Only when horse and rider had dwindled to a mere speck in the distance did she finally find the strength of will to make her limbs move.

On her feet she felt sick and shaky and desperately unhappy. Logan didn't love her; he had never loved her. It had all been a figment of her imagination.

But the feeling inside her was no figment. She felt violated, unclean. Never again, she vowed, would she allow a man to do that to her. She was finished with sex for ever!

It was only three days later that she heard of Logan's sudden departure for Australia. Three days during which she hadn't gone near the beach. From love, her emotions had turned to a hatred so intense it coloured her every waking moment.

The dawning realisation that she might turn out to be pregnant made her feel physically ill, the thought of having to tell her parents even more so. Luckily it was only a week before she received thankful proof that she was lucky this time, but the relief in no way tempered her feelings towards the man who had given her cause for such concern. Had he still been around, she would have found some way of paying him back for what he had done to her...

Which she would still if he made any attempt to come near her again, Caryn vowed to herself, returning to the present, although quite what, she wasn't sure. She could hardly go and tell a dying woman just what kind of a louse her son was.

What she had to do was put the whole affair behind her and get on with her life. Logan Bannister wasn't worth losing any sleep over.

CHAPTER TWO

SUNDAY was long and quiet. Restless still, Caryn took advantage of the continuing good weather to go for an afternoon stroll into town.

The sun had brought out the holidaymakers in force. For the first time in weeks the main beach was a scene of activity. Some hardy souls had even ventured into the sea, braving a water temperature that made Caryn shiver just thinking about it. She never attempted to swim in the sea before August even in a good season.

At four o'clock, having seen almost no one she knew, she set off to walk the couple of miles back home, not looking forward to the dull evening ahead. Her father was right, of course, she acknowledged wryly. She did spend far too much time on her own. The problem was finding someone she wanted to share that time with.

Apart from Jane, she didn't have a lot in common with her contemporaries, who seemed to spend most of their time either visiting various public houses or attending discos where the loudness of the music drowned all attempts at conversation. Other than the cinema, or a trip to one of the Norwich theatres, that was about it, she supposed.

It had been different when she'd been going out with Michael Sinclair those few weeks. He had introduced her to another world. She had refused to see him again after Logan left, and had no idea at all of where he might be these days. Not that it mattered anyway.

Reaching the crossroads on the outskirts of the town proper, she took advantage of a gap in the traffic to save waiting for the green man to put in an appearance. A misjudgement, she realised immediately, hearing the sudden blare of a horn from a car that seemed to have appeared from nowhere.

Hurrying to get across, she stumbled on the kerb and almost fell her length, hitting one knee against the stone edge with sickening force as she went down. She was vaguely aware of hearing a car door slam, and then there were hands under her arms, lifting her back into her feet.

'Thanks,' she said wryly, trying to ignore the pain from her knee. 'That was stupid of me.'

Her voice died in her throat as she turned her head to glance at her rescuer, the apologetic little smile freezing on her lips.

'Yes, it was,' agreed Logan briefly. 'You gave yourself a nasty crack. How does it feel?'

'It's nothing,' Caryn assured him, recovering her tongue if not her equilibrium. 'I'm fine!'

'I'm sure,' he returned with satire. 'You'd better get in the car and I'll run you home.'

'I said I'm all right!' she snapped. 'I don't have far to go, in any case.'

'St Albans, isn't it? We have to pass the end of your road.' His tone was unequivocal.

For the first time, Caryn became aware of the woman occupying the passenger seat of the silver blue Mercedes drawn into the roadside. Dark-haired like her son, Helen Bannister was well enough known by sight around the town, if not exactly on intimate terms with the general population. She was watching the scene now with a curious expression on a face that already showed signs of deterioration in health by its lack of colour and hollow cheeks.

'I think you had better do as Logan says,' she called through the opened window.

Logan settled the matter by taking Caryn's arm in a firm grasp and propelling her over to the car, leaving her with no alternative, short of causing a scene, but to slide into the rear passenger seat when he opened the door for her.

'Put the belt on,' he instructed. 'It might only be a few minutes' ride, but better to be safe than sorry.'

Safe enough in body, perhaps, Caryn thought hollowly. Fate played some dirty tricks.

Seated right behind Logan as he put the car into motion again, she was too close for comfort. The crisp, clean line of his hair across the nape of his neck made her ache with the longing to reach out and touch. Nothing had changed. Not where her senses were concerned. Everything about him made her ache.

Helen Bannister half turned in her seat to offer a somewhat reticent smile. 'Such a lovely day for a walk after all that rain!'

'Yes, it is.' Caryn could find nothing to add to the abrupt affirmative. None of this was Mrs Bannister's fault, she reminded herself. The woman could have no idea of the underlying currents between her son and this stranger he had picked up from the roadside. So far as she was concerned, he was simply playing the Good Samaritan.

'You must be in a lot of pain after a knock like that,' continued the other. 'Knees are always the worst places to injure.'

Caryn forced a smile of her own. 'It really isn't hurting very much at all,' she lied. 'It was my own fault anyway. I should have waited for the green light.'

Logan made no comment, but she could sense his glance through the driving mirror, imagine his sardonic expression. They were already approaching the turn-off from the main road. He took it without hesitation, as also the next turn into St Albans, drawing to a halt in front of the Gregory residence.

'Here you are,' he said. 'Safe, if not exactly sound. You should get that knee seen to. You might have chipped the bone.'

'I will,' she affirmed, hoping no one happened to be looking out of the front windows at present. 'Thank you for the lift.'

'I'll help you out,' he said as she reached for the door-handle. 'At the very least it will have stiffened up.'

He was right, Caryn discovered, biting off an exclamation as she moved her leg. Perhaps not chipped, but certainly badly bruised. Fortunately her job didn't call for a lot of walking.

Logan came back to open the door and extend a hand. She took it with reluctance, relinquishing it again the moment she was out of the car and standing on the kerb. Turning her head, she directed a brief smile at the other occupant.

'Goodbye—and thank you too.'

Mrs Bannister nodded but didn't speak. She looked, Caryn thought fleetingly, as if she scarcely knew what to say.

Logan made no further attempt to touch her in any way. Wearing a soft leather jacket in light tan, and silky roll-necked sweater, he looked every inch the landed gentry. Only on the surface, though, she reminded herself. Underneath he was pure dross.

'I need to talk to you,' he said in low but urgent tones.

Body tensed, nerves stretched, she said jerkily, 'I don't think we have anything to talk about.'

'Yes, we do.' He paused, added with purpose, 'You wouldn't want me to come to the house, I assume?'

Her head lifted sharply. 'No!'

'Then meet me tonight on the beach. Seven o'clock. Same place.'

He was gone before she could say yea or nay, rounding the car bonnet to slide back behind the wheel. Mrs Bannister lifted a hand in farewell as the vehicle moved off.

Staring after it, Caryn wondered what on earth Logan could have to say to her that hadn't already been said last night. Nothing she wanted to hear, at any rate, so he could wait in vain.

On the other hand, he might very well keep his threat to come to the house if she failed to keep the appointment, and how would she explain that to her parents? She had no choice but to go, regardless of how she might feel about it. He had made sure of that.

It was something of a relief to find that her arrival had gone unwitnessed. Her knee was painful, and as Logan had warned, already stiffening up, but she managed not to limp on her way upstairs to view the damage.

Just badly bruised, she judged from a cursory inspection. It would probably be black and blue by morning, so short skirts were definitely out. Fortunately, fashion didn't dictate any particular length at present.

They ate at six, as they always did on a Sunday. Right up until ten to seven, Caryn was vacillating over keeping her appointment with Logan. She reached a final decision on the strength of curiosity alone—or so she told herself.

Her announcement that she was going for another walk drew no particular comment. Her mother was ensconced in front of the television for her favourite situation comedy show, her father was still engrossed in the Sunday newspapers—the two of them settled into comfortable middle-age. Nothing wrong with that, Caryn supposed, yet tonight it somehow seemed indicative of everything she didn't want for herself. Life was for living, not stagnating. It was high time she gave some serious thought towards exchanging one for the other.

She was at the appointed place on the hour, to find the stretch of beach empty of all but the gulls. By ten past she had begun to think the whole thing had been Logan's sick idea of a joke, although what possible entertainment he might get from that she couldn't begin to imagine. She was on the verge of leaving when she saw horse and rider finally approaching.

Logan came up at a fast canter, drawing to a halt far enough away to avoid showering her with sand kicked up by the chestnut's hooves.

'Thanks for waiting,' he said, dismounting. 'I had a call from Australia.'

Caryn retained her seat on the ledge of sand as he moved towards her. 'I only came because you made it impossible to refuse,' she said stonily. 'Not because I want to be here. Just say what you have to say.'

He contemplated her in silence for a lengthy moment, eyes veiled. When he did speak it was with an odd note in his voice. 'I need to know how you really feel about me now, Caryn.'

The question dried her throat. She gazed at him with darkened eyes, fighting the almost overwhelming urge to jump up and rake her nails down that lean brown cheek. 'How would you expect me to feel?' she got out with an effort.

His smile was wry. 'What I'd expect and what I can hope for are two different things.'

Her voice seemed to be coming from a long way away. 'So what do you hope for?'

'That you'll be prepared to marry me,' he said.

This couldn't be for real, she thought dazedly. He was making fun of her. He had to be!

'Don't look so stricken,' he said on a dry note. 'All I'm asking for is a simple yes or no.'

'*All*?' She drew in a shaky breath. 'I don't know what kind of game you think you're playing, but you're not doing it with me!'

He caught her arm as she began to turn away, pulling her back round to face him and holding her there, a look of determination on his face. 'It's no game, believe me. I need you, Caryn.'

Need, not love, a part of her mind registered, but the shock was still too great to take any real account of the distinction.

'I don't understand,' she managed to get out. 'Why now?'

His lips twisted. 'Because you're eighteen, not sixteen. Old enough to know your own mind.'

Eyes wide and dark, she gazed at him in silence as she grappled with the implications of that statement. When she did find her voice it came out low and husky. 'Are you trying to tell me you felt the same way two years ago?'

'Why else do you think I went away?' he asked. 'You were sixteen, I was thirty-one. I doubt if your parents would have sanctioned marriage between us—whatever the circumstances.'

He was right about that, Caryn knew. They would have been utterly devastated had they been forced to learn of her premature initiation into womanhood, but there would have been no marriage. Not at sixteen. She searched the firm features with a sense almost of desperation, heart and mind in turmoil. Right at this moment she didn't know how she felt about him—about anything. It was all too much to take in.

As if in recognition of her dilemma, he drew her to him, sliding a hand behind her head to tilt her face up to his. The kiss moved her immeasurably in its gentle yet inexorable seeking. She found her arms moving of their own accord up about his neck, her whole body surging into closer proximity. There had never been anyone else who could make her feel this way—as if fireworks had been lit inside her. She wanted him to go on kissing her, to make love to her, to lift her to that seventh heaven she had experienced so briefly yet never once forgotten.

It was Logan himself who brought matters to a halt by putting her firmly, if with reluctance, away from him. He was smiling, eyes fired with a desire he made no effort to conceal.

'Still the same lovely, warm, responsive Caryn,' he murmured. 'I've dreamed about making love to you again, but it isn't going to happen like this. We have a lot to talk about first.'

Still held fast in the grip of her turbulent emotions, Caryn allowed herself to be drawn to a seat on the wedge

of sand she had so recently vacated. Logan kept an arm
lightly about her shoulders.

'Before we go any further,' he said, 'I have to tell you
that my mother knows the whole story, and has done
from the start. She kept an eye on you for me. If there
had been any hint at all of a pregnancy, I would have
come back and faced up to it, but going away seemed
the best thing for us both at the time.'

Caryn said slowly, 'Does she know about . . . now?'

'Yes.'

'And approves?'

'Yes,' he said again, and hesitated a moment before
continuing, 'She's the main reason I'm not prepared to
spend too much time rebuilding a relationship between
us. It's her dearest wish to see me happily married.' There
was a pause, a change of tone. 'You are going to marry
me, aren't you, Caryn?'

'It's all so sudden,' she protested. 'I can't take it in.'
She could feel herself trembling as reaction began to set
in. 'You didn't attempt to see me last year when your
father died.'

'I dared not let myself. I was only here a few days,
anyway.' He brought up his other hand to trace the line
of her mouth with the tip of a finger, making her tremble
with another, quite different emotion. 'You told me once
that you loved me,' he said softly. 'Does that still follow?'

Caryn was hard put to it to think of anything other
than what he was doing to her with that slow caress. She
caught at his hand, staying the movement yet not pulling
away. 'We hardly know one another,' she whispered.
'Not in any real sense.'

'We know how we feel,' he returned. 'That's the
most important.'

Caryn wasn't sure. She felt totally confused. For this to happen after two years of hatred was beyond all reason. How could she even begin to sort out her emotions?

'Does your mother really consider me the kind of wife you should have?' she asked. 'There must be others far more suitable.'

'Suitable to whom, and for what?' Logan queried. 'If I'm going to take a wife at all, then it has to be my choice.'

He studied her for a brief moment, then tilted her chin and kissed her again, this time with less restraint, parting her lips in surging response. Caryn didn't try to think, only to feel—the way she had always felt about this man deep down in her heart. He had been her first love; she wanted him to be her only love. Nothing else seemed important right now but that.

'I take it the answer is yes,' he said with a touch of arrogance when he lifted his head at last. 'It must be soon. There isn't a lot of time left.'

'It can't be *that* soon.' She was breathless, heart racing, mind in a whirl. 'What do I tell my parents?'

'The truth, up to a point,' he suggested. 'Just leave out the more intimate detail. They'll surely understand the need for haste when they know about Mother.'

'She won't mind their knowing?'

'Providing they keep it to themselves. The last thing she'd want is for the whole town to know.' Logan took her hand, pressing the back of it to his lips in a gesture that warmed her all the way through. 'You're of age. It's your decision, not theirs. *Your* life.' His smile was an inducement in itself. 'You won't regret it, Caryn. I'll make sure you don't.'

Caution went to the winds. Whatever the cost, she thought recklessly, she couldn't turn her back on this dream come true. Logan had to love her, even though he hadn't actually used the word. How else could he contemplate marriage?

'Yes,' she breathed, not trying to keep her emotions in check any longer. 'Yes, Logan, I'll marry you. As soon as you like!'

He made no attempt to kiss her again, much as she wanted him to. His acknowledging nod was verging on the perfunctory. 'Give me half an hour to return Ballantyne to the stables, and I'll come and see your parents,' he said. 'Or better still, why don't you come on back with me, then we can drive in together?'

It was all going too fast, much too fast, but Caryn wouldn't allow herself pause for reflection. Logan was in charge all the way; that was how she wanted it. It was how she had always wanted it.

He put her up before him on the horse, the same way he had that other evening. Only this was different, so different, she thought blissfully, leaning against him. She could feel the strong beat of his heart through the two layers of clothing, the radiating body heat. The muscles of her inner thighs went into spasm at the memory of that other time. Such an age ago, but never forgotten. And soon to happen again, if Logan had his way. Only this time they would be man and wife.

Whitegates lay back from the coastal road. Built of mellow brick, and Georgian in design, the house was large and imposing, the formal gardens immediately surrounding it full of life and colour. The stables lay off to the rear, reached via a lane running alongside the property, with the seventy acres of privately owned land stretching beyond.

A youth came out to the yard to take the horse as Logan handed Caryn down from its back. She knew him by sight if not by name, and was aware that he recognised her too from the way he gaped at her.

'You can talk to Mother while I get out of these things,' said Logan, turning her back towards the house. 'It won't take me long.'

'What do I say to her?' Caryn asked, panicking at the very thought of facing the woman.

'Just be yourself,' he advised. 'She won't bite.' He gave her a reassuring smile. 'She wants this as much as I do.'

Neither of them more than she did herself, came the fervent thought as she looked up into the lean features. She belonged to this man, wholly and for ever. Time had no bearing. A day, a week, a year, even two years—it was all the same.

They went in through a side door, passing along a corridor to emerge into a lofty hall panelled in oak. The staircase rose from the centre, branching off at the halfway point to galleried landings either side. Black and white tiles polished to a high but non-slippery sheen covered the floor.

Glancing around, Caryn felt intimidated by the obvious signs of wealth allied to superb good taste, conscious of her simple cotton trousers and shirt, her windblown hair. Even in jodhpurs and riding boots, Logan looked completely at home.

He crossed to double doors on the right and ushered her through to a room full of soft evening light. A beautiful room, full of antiques yet with a lived-in look that gave her fresh heart. Seated on a brocade sofa by the side of the white marble fireplace, Mrs Bannister welcomed the two of them with a smile that seemed wholly genuine.

'I gather that congratulations are in order?' she said to her son. To Caryn, she added, 'Come and sit by me. We have to get to know one another.'

'I'll leave you to it,' said Logan. 'I'm going up to change.'

Stay, Caryn wanted to beg, but he was already closing the door in his wake. Feeling totally at a loss, she moved to do his mother's bidding, perching on the very edge of her seat.

'Do make yourself comfortable,' the older woman invited. 'I realise how difficult this must be for you, but I can assure you that I thoroughly approve my son's choice.'

'But you don't even know me,' Caryn pointed out bemusedly.

'I know of you—and of your family. The Gregorys are very well respected.' She paused as if to choose her words, eyes reflective as they dwelt on the face turned towards her. 'You're very young. The only question I would ask is, are you quite sure this is what *you* want?'

'Oh, yes!' Caryn could say that without hesitation. She gave a laugh. 'I'm still reeling from the suddenness of it all, but it's definitely what I want. What I always...' She broke off, colouring and looking down at the hands clasped in her lap. 'Logan said he'd told you...everything.'

'Yes, he did. Two years ago. It was the only way he could make me understand why he had decided to accept his friend's invitation to partner him in Australia.' The tone was matter-of-fact. 'It seemed the best thing at the time.'

Caryn said softly, 'Because of me you lost your son for two years.'

'Not wholly. I visited him. In any case, he and his father didn't get along too well, so it was better for them both to be apart for a while.' Her voice briskened. 'That's all in the past. We have the future to look to now. You'll be prepared to live here at Whitegates after you're married, I trust?'

'Well, yes, of course.' Caryn hadn't got that far in her imaginings as yet, and could find no other answer.

'You'll have your own rooms, of course. The house is big enough to convert the upper east wing. Plenty of room for a nursery too.'

'Nursery?' Caryn's head came up, eyes startled. 'Isn't that looking a bit *far* ahead?'

'I hope not too far.' The smile was still there, but slightly strained now, the grey eyes so like her son's petitioning. 'I'd give a great deal to see my grandchild before I die.'

'Of course.' Caryn could think of nothing else to say. She and Logan weren't even married yet. If they were to grant his mother's wish, they would have to move fast. She felt disconcerted by the request, even while she could appreciate the motives behind it. Everything was moving too fast.

She was relieved when Logan came back into the room. He had exchanged the jodhpurs for linen trousers and a fine cotton shirt in a pale green that enhanced his tan. Her heart jolted at the very sight of him. It just didn't seem possible that he was to be her husband.

'Ready?' he said. 'Let's go and get it over with.'

For the first time Caryn allowed herself to consider the shock they were about to drop on her parents. How on earth did she make them understand?

'It's too soon,' she heard herself saying apprehensively. 'They never even met you before!'

'They'll adjust,' Logan declared firmly. 'They'll have to adjust.'

'Logan will take care of it,' his mother assured her.

Caryn came to her feet with reluctance. Logan might, but she would still have to face her family after he had gone. They were going to be devastated, disbelieving. How could they be anything else in the circumstances?

'I'll see you again soon,' said Mrs Bannister. She looked tired, her face pale. 'Very soon.'

They were in the Mercedes and heading down the drive before Caryn found her tongue. 'I think I'm going to wake up and find this is all a dream,' she said, unsurprised to hear the quiver in her voice.

Logan looked amused. 'Would you like me to pinch you to prove you're awake? It's real enough, I can assure you.'

She glanced at him sideways as he brought the car to a halt before turning out on to the road, viewing the clean-cut profile with an undeniable thril! of excitement. He moved the car out from the drive, and accelerated away, hands firm on the wheel. Good hands, thought Caryn, watching their movement; long and lean and knowledgeable, the nails neatly trimmed and clean-rimmed. If he was nervous, he certainly wasn't revealing it. He looked totally at ease.

Sensing her scrutiny, he glanced her way with a brief smile. 'Don't worry about it. I'll do the talking.'

It wasn't a long journey. Caryn knew a wave of sheer panic when Logan brought the car to a halt at the front gate. She fought it down, but could feel herself trembling inside when she got out of the vehicle.

'Bear up,' said Logan softly, closing the door. He slid an arm about her shoulders and drew her close for a moment, his lips warm against her temple. 'It will be all right, you'll see.'

Eventually, perhaps, she thought, but it was the here and now that had to be got through first.

The front door was unlocked, the way it usually was during the day despite all the warnings. Susan Gregory came out from the living-room as Caryn closed the door again.

'You've been a long...' she began, breaking off abruptly on taking in Logan's presence. Surprise gave way to confusion as her gaze moved from his face back to her daughter's, then her natural good manners took over. 'Mr Bannister, isn't it? From Whitegates?'

'That's right,' he returned easily. 'And the name is Logan. I'm sorry to spring things on you this way, but better sooner than later.'

The confusion grew. 'I don't understand. What things?'

He indicated the room from which she had just emerged. 'I think you and your husband should hear it together.'

Throat dry as a bone, Caryn felt his hand at her centre back ushering her ahead of him into the room in her mother's wake. Her father looked at the newcomer in surprise, then questioningly at Caryn.

'Is there something wrong?' he asked.

Face registering little, Logan reached out an arm and drew Caryn to his side in a gesture unmistakably possessive. 'Before anything else, we should tell you that we're going to be married.'

The silence following that forthright announcement seemed to Caryn to stretch interminably. The two stunned faces gazing back at them looked to be carved from stone. John Gregory was the first to recover his power of speech.

'Isn't this a bit sudden?' he asked on an amazingly mild note. 'I know who you are, but I wasn't aware that you and Caryn knew each other. Didn't you just get back from Australia or somewhere?'

'That's right,' Logan said again. 'Only yesterday. I've waited two years. I wasn't prepared to wait any longer. It would be nice to have your blessing.'

Nice, but by no means essential, his tone suggested—to Caryn at least. She kept her eyes fixed on her father's face, neither caring nor daring to glance in her mother's direction.

'I know it has to be a shock for you both,' she said huskily, thinking that that had to be the understatement of the year. 'It was for me too. But it's what I want. More than anything in the world!'

'I don't understand,' said her mother blankly. 'It doesn't make any sense! You were just a schoolgirl two years ago!'

'Which is why I went away when I did,' put in Logan smoothly. 'To give her time to grow up. Even if you'd been willing to grant approval then, which I very much doubt, I couldn't have traded on a sixteen-year-old's feelings. Fortunately, Caryn still feels the same way. We want to be together.'

'Are you saying you were seeing each other while she was still in school?' demanded Susan on a shocked note. 'You must be nearly old enough to be her father!'

The dark head inclined, mouth wryly slanted. 'Possible, if unlikely. Caryn was a very mature schoolgirl in a lot of ways. We shared a lot of interests.'

'Michael Sinclair introduced us at a family party,' said Caryn swiftly. 'You remember Michael?'

'Of course I remember Michael. You brought *him* to meet us.' Susan's voice had sharpened. 'This is quite ridiculous!'

'I think the two of you had better sit down,' said John Gregory. 'You too, Susan,' he added to his wife. 'We have to discuss this.'

'There's nothing very much to discuss,' Logan returned. 'Apart from wedding arrangements perhaps. It would probably be easier all round if we made it the register office rather than a church ceremony. Easier and quicker. Before the end of the month for preference.'

'Now just wait a minute!' Relatively calm up to now, the older man was beginning to sound agitated. 'Everything else aside, what's the rush? You haven't been back five minutes!'

'There's a good reason,' said Caryn, deciding it was time she put in a word. She glanced at Logan, taking his nod as recognition and approval of what she was about to impart. 'Mrs Bannister doesn't have long to live,' she went on, trying to sound as matter-of-fact about it as the woman herself had been earlier. 'She naturally wants to see Logan settled before she goes. The longer we wait, the weaker she's going to become.' She paused, looking from one parent to the other in an appeal for understanding. '*I* don't want to wait either.'

'I'm sorry about your mother,' said Susan Gregory to Logan on a subdued note. 'I heard she'd been ill, but I had no idea it was so bad.'

'She's accepted it,' he returned levelly. 'But you can appreciate that I'd want her to be as happy as possible while she's still with us, and this will help.'

'Does she already know about it?'

Caryn took it on herself to answer that question too. 'Logan took me to see her before we came on here.'

'It's a wonder the shock didn't kill her!'

'She's always known how I felt about Caryn,' answered Logan without particular inflection. 'I realise how you must both of you be feeling, and I'm sorry it has to be this way, but that's the way it is. Caryn is happy about it. I'd like you to be too.'

The arm about Caryn's shoulders increased pressure for a fleeting moment, then was removed. 'I think the best thing is for me to leave now and give you all chance to talk in private. Tomorrow will be time enough to start discussing arrangements.' To Caryn herself, he added on a softer note, 'Come and see me off.'

She accompanied him wordlessly, reluctant to have him go so soon, even while she recognised the motive behind his departure. She had to face her family alone some time, so why prolong the agony?

'I'll see you tomorrow,' he said at the door. 'You have to get to know your future home.'

'I'm at work tomorrow,' she reminded him, and saw his expression alter.

'I'd forgotten about your job. Are you monthly or weekly salaried?'

'Weekly,' she acknowledged. 'But——'

'Then you only need give a week's notice. I'd propose that we arrange the wedding for the twenty-ninth. That's a week from Wednesday. I can only spare a few days for a honeymoon, but we can take a longer break later.'

Caryn's head was reeling. He had it all planned. Every last detail! And why not? came the thought. Wasn't it better to have a man who knew exactly what he wanted and did something about it than one who left everything to others? She had always known him for a forceful character; she wouldn't want him any different. And hadn't she been saying only yesterday that she found her job boring? Life as Logan's wife would be infinitely more exciting!

'I'll hand my notice in first thing,' she promised. She gave a sudden laugh. 'It's going to cause quite a furore when I tell them the reason!'

Logan smiled and shrugged. 'A nine-day wonder. They'll get over it.' Bending his head, he placed a brief and unsatisfying kiss on her mouth, leaving her aching for more. 'You'd better go on back and face the music,' he said. 'I'll be here tomorrow evening.'

He was gone before she could protest, pulling the door closed behind him. Caryn stood for a moment or two gathering herself before returning to the living room. Nothing anyone could say or do was going to change her mind, she vowed. She would marry Logan come what may! As he had said, it was her life, her choice.

All the same, facing the two of them was one of the hardest things she had ever done in her life. Looking from one accusing face to another, she sought defence in a direct frontal attack.

'I *do* know what I'm doing, and I'm of age to do it,' she declared, 'so please don't try telling me any different. I was in love with Logan two years ago, and I am still.'

'You were too young to be in love with anybody two years ago,' said her mother flatly. 'You were infatuated with an older man.'

'Call it what you like,' Caryn returned defiantly. 'I know how I felt then, and I know how I feel now.'

'And what about Bannister?' asked her father without raising his voice. 'Are you as sure of his feelings?'

'Of course. Why else would he want to marry me?'

Susan made a helpless little gesture. 'I still can't take it all in. You never even mentioned his name before!'

Caryn felt the defiance crumble. She crossed swiftly to her mother and pressed a kiss on her cheek. 'It's going to be all right. It really is. I love him.'

'A man nearly twice your age!'

'I'd feel the same way whatever age he was.' She tried to lighten the atmosphere with a joke. 'And you have to admit, he's an awfully good catch!'

'There's a great deal more to marriage than money,' said her mother sharply, taking the remark at face value. 'How do you know you can trust him? He had quite a reputation in the past.'

'If he had, it's in the past,' Caryn responded, refusing to allow the intimation to bother her. 'I'd be far more worried if he hadn't already sown his wild oats, as the saying goes.' She made an appealing gesture to her father. 'I'm sorry for springing it on you this way, but please try to understand. I love Logan, I'm going to marry him, and I want you to be happy for me.'

'If he cares enough for you,' said John Gregory slowly, 'he'll be prepared to wait a while.'

'Regardless of his mother's condition?' Caryn shook her head. 'It wouldn't make any difference, anyway.' She paused, looking from one to the other of her parents. 'You won't refuse to have anything to do with the wedding, will you?'

'Meaning you'll be going ahead with it whether we do or not.' Her father's tone was wry. 'No, we won't refuse. How could we turn our backs on our own daughter?'

'Thanks.' Caryn hardly knew what else to say. 'I think I'll have another early night,' she tagged on, anxious to escape any further discussion. 'I'll be giving in my notice tomorrow, by the way. Logan doesn't want a working wife.'

She made her escape before any comment could be made, and went straight upstairs to her room, sitting down on the end of bed to contemplate her reflection in the dressing-table mirror. Love not only made the world go round, it also improved one's looks, she decided, viewing her bright eyes and glowing skin. Confidence, that was the key. With Logan to inspire it in her, she could handle any situation that came along.

CHAPTER THREE

ON THE face of it, the wedding went off without a hitch. Susan would have preferred that it take place in church, but with no dates available until well into August, Logan had refused to wait.

He had made the arrangements himself, and insisted on paying the bills. With personal savings at a low ebb, and an utter dread of being in any kind of debt, John Gregory had been forced to pocket his pride and let matters take their course.

Despite every precaution, news of the impending nuptials had spread through the town like greased lightening. Emerging from the register office to find a whole crowd of well-wishers hanging around the doorstep, Caryn put on a brave face and tried to ignore the fact that most of them were here out of curiosity alone, not through any genuine interest.

Apart from Jane, she had invited no one outside her own immediate family. Logan, however, had extended his list to include several friends. It had been quite a shock to see Margot and Duncan Ashley among them, although the former appeared happy enough to be there. Wearing apricot silk, she outshone every other woman in the place—including the bride herself in Caryn's own estimation.

In place of a formal reception, they were to eat a buffet luncheon out at Whitegates. Later, she and Logan would leave for the Cotswolds, where they were to spend what she knew would be an idyllic few days at a small but exclusive country hotel he knew of. Caryn could well understand his reluctance to leave his mother alone for any longer time under the circumstances. Less than a year, the medics had said, but that could mean more or less any time.

'Happy?' he asked, when they gained the comparative privacy of the hired limousine at last.

'Totally,' she said, closing her mind on the image of her parents standing there so forlornly on the pavement. They were to follow on in one of the other cars.

'They'll get used to it,' Logan advised, taking an accurate guess at her thoughts as her face clouded a little. 'It isn't as if you're going to be far away.'

Caryn summoned a smile, a shake of her head. 'I know.' She looked out through the windscreen at the sunlit streets, feeling a swelling sense of wellbeing. 'I hope this weather keeps up—for the next few days at least.'

Logan's smile was slow. 'I dare say we can find ways to entertain ourselves even if it doesn't.'

The very thought of what was to come doubled her pulse-rate. There had been no opportunity over the past few days to indulge that desire they both so obviously shared, nor would she have wanted to do so. What she wanted was a wedding-night to remember—the first time of sharing a bed with the man she loved. It had been a wonderful experience two years ago, but tonight would be better still. Tonight there would be no shattering comedown, no heartbreak to be gone through. Tonight, and all the other nights to come, Logan would make love to her as her husband. They would be together for all time.

'I'm glad Margot came,' she said impulsively. 'It shows she bears you no grudges.'

'She has no reason to,' Logan answered levelly. 'She knew I was leaving.'

Caryn gave him a swift sideways glance. 'But not why, I hope.'

'Of course not. It was enough for me to know.'

'It wasn't really your fault,' she said generously. 'I was absolutely shameless.'

'Absolutely,' he agreed, smiling as she wrinkled her nose at him. 'And utterly irresistible with it.'

The glass partition cutting them off from the driver gave her the confidence to answer in kind. 'I hope you still find me the same.'

'You'll have the answer to that tonight.' He laughed as she coloured up. 'All legal and above board this time.'

'It was last time,' she said. 'Legal, I mean. I was above the age of consent.'

'Only just.' He slid an arm about her, drawing her close to plant a light kiss on her temple. 'That's just to be going on with, Mrs Bannister.'

Mrs Bannister! It sounded so strange. Wonderful too, though, she thought exultantly, revelling in the warmth of his embrace. Man and wife, that was what they were. Till death them did part.

Whitegates' live-in domestic staff consisted of a middle-aged couple by the name of Lawson who had a flat over the garages. Mrs Lawson had prepared the whole luncheon herself, and done a splendid job. Not that Caryn felt like eating, although she made herself eat something in order to soak up the champagne.

The short cream coat-dress she had chosen to be married in was practical enough for travelling, so she had elected not to bother changing for the journey. Logan, however, was not happy to travel in the grey suit he had worn for the occasion, so around three o'clock he disappeared upstairs to don some less formal attire.

With her parents engaged in conversation with Mrs Bannister, and Jane already gone to keep a date with Roy Gillingham, Caryn found herself momentarily alone. Margot came to join her, a smile on her lips as she raised her glass in salute.

'I came to wish you luck,' she said lightly. 'You're going to need it.'

Caryn's own smile faltered as she registered the malice in the green eyes. She had been wrong. Margot did bear grudges. But against her, it seemed, not Logan.

'I already have it,' she said, rallying her forces. 'But thanks for the thought.'

Margot laughed pityingly, the malice even more pronounced. 'You really don't know, do you? About the condition Logan's father made, I mean?' She didn't bother waiting for a reply. 'He had until this coming weekend to find himself a wife, or lose everything. It seems the old man thought he needed a stabilising influence, although he'd hardly have considered an eighteen-year-old capable of providing it, I'm sure.'

It was true, thought Caryn numbly in that following frozen moment. Logan had said it himself that very first evening. A condition he hadn't been prepared to fulfil at the time of his father's death, but which his mother's illness had made imperative. 'Now I must,' those had been his words.

In the space of a few seconds her whole world had been torn apart again. There lay the real reason behind Logan's urgency. Without a wife he couldn't lay claim to the estate. He didn't love her. He had simply taken advantage of a readily available solution to the problem.

But there were surely plenty of others who would have
been more than ready to help him solve his dilemma?
came the thought, bringing a momentary halt to the dis-
integration. Perhaps so, suggested another and unsus-
pectedly cynical part of her mind, but who else as
malleable? Who else prepared to allow him total domi-
nance? Who else, if it came to that, as unlikely to cause
too much trouble when it came to getting rid in time to
come—as he no doubt planned to do once his mother
was out of the way.

Deep down, she had never really trusted him. She knew
that now. She had simply closed out the doubts. But she
couldn't do that any more. The truth had to be faced.
She was a means to an end, no more.

From somewhere she found the control to smile, to
say lightly, 'Oh, *that* condition! I thought you were
talking about something else. Of course I knew. Why
else do you think I was willing to settle for such a hurried
affair?'

Margot didn't believe her; she could see that from her
expression. All the same, she felt the need to go on pretending. She even tried a laugh, surprising herself with
the sound. 'Logan isn't the only one to gain, after all.'

'He will be,' came the cynical reply. 'You can be sure
of that.'

Right now she was sure of only one thing, Caryn reflected, feeling the pain and humiliation spreading
through her as the older woman moved away. This was
the second time Logan had used her, but it would be the
last. He was going to discover just how wrong he had
been in his assessment!

How and when she was going to tell him what she had
discovered, she wasn't sure, but tell him she would. To
all intents and purposes this marriage was over before

it had begun, because she certainly wouldn't be sharing a bed with him tonight—or any other night. In fact, he could go to the Cotswolds on his own!

And was she prepared to explain why to her parents and Mrs Bannister? she asked herself hollowly at that point. But the latter would already know of the clause, she realised in the next breath. She had to know. It explained so much. Her desire to see her son married before she died was only a part of it. In order to see him inherit, she had been forced to accept whoever he picked out as the likeliest prospect for a speedy wooing.

Whatever, she was still a dying woman, and therefore to be excused a whole lot. With regard to her parents, Caryn shuddered to think of the effect such a revelation would have on them. She couldn't do it to them. Certainly not here and now. Which left her with little alternative but to carry the charade through.

Logan put in an appearance some minutes later looking relaxed and casual in sports jacket and light trousers.

'Our cases are in the car,' he said. 'We may as well be on our way.'

Caryn kept a smile fixed to her face for appearances, aware of Margot's close interest from across the room. 'There's no rush, is there? It can't be much more than a couple of hours to where we're going.'

'It depends on what traffic conditions we meet.' Logan's tone was easy, but the grey eyes were decisive. 'There's no point in lingering any longer.'

'I think I might change first after all,' she declared, looking for any way to delay the moment when the two of them would be alone. 'I'll be too warm in this in the car.'

'If you are, we can have the air-conditioning on,' he returned reasonably.

Caryn had forgotten about that, but she wasn't about to be pressured. It was an effort to keep the smile going. 'All the same, I'd like to change.'

For a moment he seemed on the verge of putting his foot down, then he shrugged good-humouredly. 'A woman's prerogative. Just don't be long.'

Her clothes had been brought here to Whitegates the previous day, and hung away in one of the wardrobes lining the rear wall of the room they were to share on their return. A lovely room with its beautifully draped windows and fine furnishings, Caryn had thought on seeing it for the first time. Now, the sight of the double bed made her throat close up. Love her or not, Logan would obviously expect all the customary marital privileges. It was so different for a man. He didn't have to be in love to make love. The act alone was enough.

Only not with her, she thought fiercely. No way was *she* going to emulate her forebears and allow him to violate her! Because that was all it would be: a defilement of everything she held sacred. She might be stuck with this marriage for the time being, but that was as far as she was prepared to go, and Logan would have to accept it.

She had half expected him to follow her upstairs, but he didn't, much to her relief. She needed more time to gear herself up for the moment of confrontation. It had to come before they reached the hotel if she weren't to find herself confined with him for the night in a double room. He could change the reservation to singles when they got there.

Dressed in jeans and a plain cotton shirt, she made her way back down to the drawing-room. Logan lifted a quizzical eyebrow when he saw her, but made no comment. It was left to her mother to express a reaction to her appearance.

'You can't seriously intend to go on honeymoon like that!' she exclaimed in horror. 'What on earth possessed you?'

Caryn kept her tone light, her expression unconcerned. 'I'm comfortable like this. That's surely more important than looking like a dress-shop mannequin?'

'Every time,' Logan agreed. 'She looks just fine, Mrs Gregory. We're not going anywhere upmarket.' He glanced at his watch. 'We'd better be leaving. I'd like to be there before dinner.'

Everyone came out on to the forecourt to see them off. Caryn forced herself to look Margot straight in the eye as she said goodbye, determined to keep up the act until the last. The only way the other could know about the clause was if Logan himself had told her, which suggested something she didn't want to think about too deeply.

Her parents were leaving right after them, although they would be returning to Whitegates that evening for dinner at Mrs Bannister's instigation, along with some of the other guests. Neither of them was over-eager to be drawn into the Bannister social circles, so Caryn doubted if it would become a regular occurrence, for which she was thankful. It would be difficult enough handling such occasions herself—especially now with her confidence so totally shattered.

The moment of departure had to come. Sinking back into the deep comfort of the padded seat as the car turned out of the drive, she tried to blank out her thoughts and become a zombie simply going through the motions. This

should have been one of the happiest times of her life.
It didn't bear thinking about.

'You're very quiet,' Logan commented after they'd
been going for ten minutes. 'Tired?'

'I suppose I am,' she said, seizing on the excuse. 'It's
been so hectic this last week.'

'So have a sleep.' His mouth slanted. 'We wouldn't
want you nodding off over the dinner table.'

To say nothing of later, came the thought, robbing
her of any hope of forgetfulness. She closed her eyes
without answering, steeling herself to keep them closed
for as long as possible. When she opened them again,
that would be the time to say what she had to say.

Unlikely as it had seemed, she must have fallen asleep
eventually. When she did open her eyes again they were
driving along a country road with the sun angling in
through the side window. Logan had taken off his jacket
and rolled the sleeves of his shirt, so he must have
stopped the car at some point.

'Hi,' he said softly as she lifted her head from the
corner cushion of her seat. 'You really *were* tired!'

Caryn ran her tongue over lips lacking in moisture,
mind at ease for a brief moment before memory came
flooding back. She felt physically sick from the anguish
of that realisation.

'What time is it?' she got out.

'Just gone six o'clock,' he advised. 'We made good
time. We should be there in half an hour or so.'

Caryn took a deep steadying breath, knowing she
could leave it no longer. 'You'd better stop the car,' she
said tonelessly. 'I have something to say to you.'

Logan gave her a swift glance, a line appearing between the dark brows as he registered her set expression.
'So say it.'

'Not while you're driving,' she insisted.

There was a parking sign just coming up on their side of the road. He signalled and braked to take the turn-off, bringing the car to a halt halfway round the tree-fringed lay-by and switching off the engine. Apart from one other vehicle parked further along, which appeared to be empty, they were on their own.

'Fire away,' he invited.

There was only one way to say it, and that was straight out. 'Margot told me about the will.'

His reaction was not what she had anticipated: no guilt, just a wry twist of the lips. 'You had to find out eventually, although I hoped to do the telling myself. Dad apparently made no secret of it.'

Caryn gazed at him in numbed silence for a moment, aware now that deep down she had been hoping for a denial—to hear it was all a lie; a sick joke on Margot's part. 'So it's true,' she forced out. 'You only married me to fulfil the condition.'

The grey eyes remained steady. 'It's true that I had to rush the wedding plans in order to stay within the time limit set, yes, but that doesn't mean I didn't want to marry you.'

'I don't believe you.' The words were torn from her. 'You had to find someone in a hurry, and I was the easiest prospect. Naïve, gullible, besotted Caryn Gregory!' She jerked away as he made a move towards her. 'Don't touch me!'

Face suddenly grim, he sat back again in his seat. 'So I wasn't totally honest with you. I couldn't take the risk of having you think what you're thinking now, and turning me down.'

'What else am I supposed to think?' Caryn demanded bitterly. 'You knew how I felt about you, and you traded on it—the same way you traded on it two years ago!'

'That's not true.' Logan was in control of himself, jaw rigid. 'I lost my head over you two years ago, and paid the price. The reason my father chose to make that condition was because he believed I needed an anchor. If I hadn't found one within a year of knowing about it, then I wasn't going to.'

He paused, studying her, expression softening a little. 'Caryn, if all I'd wanted was to inherit I'd have either fulfilled the terms before this or fought the will through the courts. If it weren't for my mother's illness I'd have allowed things to stand the way they were, with everything going to charity on her eventual death. I'd made a life for myself in Australia. A good life. I didn't need the stud, or anything else.'

She said thickly, 'It doesn't alter anything. If it weren't for your mother's illness you wouldn't have come back at all, much less asked me to marry you.' She searched the lean features, looking for something she knew she wasn't going to find. 'Would you?'

His hesitation was all the answer she needed. She groped blindly for the door-handle, hardly knowing where she intended going. All she wanted was to get away from this man who had suddenly become anathema to her.

The hand which fastened on her upper arm was firm rather than rough, but effective in staying her flight. Logan released her as she subsided back into her seat, but remained obviously poised for any further attempt to leave the car.

'You're not going anywhere,' he declared. 'You're going to sit there and listen to me.'

'Telling me what?' she asked harshly. 'That you love me?'

'Is that so hard to believe?'

'Yes. You don't *use* someone you love!'

'In some circumstances there's no alternative.' His tone was level. 'It also depends on your concept of the word. If we're talking about high-flown romance then we're on different wavelengths. No, I probably wouldn't have asked you to marry me if this hadn't happened, but because of the age difference, not because I feel nothing for you.'

'Oh, I can imagine you feel *something*! You've made that obvious.' The bitterness was spilling over, lending a totally new acridity to her voice. 'Just don't imagine you're going to indulge it, that's all!'

'Meaning what?'

'Meaning we might be married but these aren't Victorian times. I don't have to do anything I don't want to do.'

'Let me get this quite straight,' he said. 'You're prepared to carry on with the marriage, but with restrictions?'

'Taking your mother's condition into consideration, to say nothing of my own parents' feelings, I don't have any choice but to carry on,' Caryn returned defensively. 'But that's as far as it goes. I won't...sleep with you, Logan.'

His smile was hard-edged. 'I'd as soon have you wide awake.'

'You know what I'm talking about.' Her voice was ragged. 'You can joke about it all you like, but I'm serious!'

'Who's joking?' He was looking at her now as if he were seeing her for the first time—and not particularly liking what he saw. 'I thought you'd grown up, but I see I was wrong. You're still the same star-struck teenager. So let's have it in bald terms, if that's what it takes. I needed to secure the estate because my mother wanted it that way, and I wasn't going to drag the family name through the courts to do it. You were the natural choice—the only choice, if it comes to that. The age gap still bothered me, but, weighed against everything else, it wasn't unsurmountable.' He shook his head as she made to speak. 'No, you hear me out. Whatever else you might or might not feel, there's one thing that hasn't changed; I could sense it in you that very first night back. Sexual attraction might not be the ideal basis for marriage, but it's an essential part of it. The rest can develop—given half a chance.'

It was Caryn's turn to shake her head, mind and heart closed to any appeal. 'Not the way I feel about you now.' She paused for emphasis, eyes dark in the pallor of her face. 'I hate you, Logan!'

His sigh held resignation. 'Now you're really being childish!' He put out a hand and fired the ignition. 'We'd better get on.'

'I want to go back.' Her voice had a tremor in it. 'There's no point in going on.'

'We've appearances to keep up, if nothing else,' he said unequivocally. 'We're booked in over the weekend, and that's how long we'll be staying.'

'Separate rooms, then,' she insisted. 'It has to be separate rooms.'

He made no answer to that. Mouth compressed, he put the car into motion with a force that spun the wheels in the gritted surface of the lay-by. Caryn closed her eyes again as they headed back to the road, not through fear of crashing, because there was no other traffic in sight, but the better to contain her utter misery.

The hotel was a picture-postcard of a place with roses round the door and clematis climbing over the walls. Sited just outside an equally picturesque village, it would have been the ideal honeymoon retreat, Caryn thought achingly as they drew up. There were four whole nights and three whole days to get through before they could return to Barston without arousing suspicion that all was not well between them. How they were going to spend the days, she had no idea, but the nights would definitely be apart.

'Have a seat while I check us in,' said Logan in the chintzy, oak-beamed lobby.

It was the first time he had spoken in half an hour, but he sounded quite normal. Nor, Caryn reflected, was there any sign of strain in the grey eyes.

'Just don't forget what I said,' she returned with what control she could muster.

His expression didn't alter. 'I haven't forgotten.'

The reception desk was set within an archway, with room for only one person at a time to receive attention. Gazing at Logan's back as he signed the register, Caryn was bound to acknowledge the effect his broad-shouldered, lean-hipped frame still had on her senses. How could slacks be called slacks when they outlined the firm male hemispheres the way they did? she found herself wondering, and pulled herself up sharply before the thought could progress. Without love to sustain it, physical attraction would soon grow stale. Logan had killed her love for him stone-dead. Nothing would ever resurrect it.

He came back to where she sat, reaching for the two suitcases, face still impassive. 'No lifts,' he said. 'We walk. It's only the one flight.'

Caryn refrained with an effort from asking about the single rooms. He would have done it; of course he would have done it. If he hadn't she would simply walk out of the place.

He carried the cases with ease, moving slightly ahead of her up the narrow staircase to reach a long landing with doors opening off to both sides. Dropping the suitcases to the floor outside the first door on the left, he took a key from his trouser pocket and inserted it in the lock, then stood back with a gesture of a hand to indicate that she should enter.

Caryn did so, registered the double bed with its flower-sprigged coverlet and came up short barely a couple of steps into the room. A firm hand in the centre of her back urged her inexorably forward. Jerking away, she turned to see Logan swing both suitcases inside before closing the door again with a foot.

'I told you——'. she began.

'I know what you told me,' he said without inflection. 'This happens to be the only room available.'

'I don't believe you. You didn't even try!'

'There was no point. It was the only key left on the board. June is a popular month. We were lucky to get a room at all at short notice.'

'Lucky!' Her voice choked. 'The *un*luckiest day of my life was the day I first clapped eyes on you! I won't share a bed with you. Not now, not ever!'

'You'll not only share a bed,' he returned grimly, 'you'll learn to act like an adult. You're not sixteen any more. Try remembering that.'

'If acting like an adult means letting you near me, I'd as soon not bother,' she flashed, stung by the scathing assertion. 'If there's no room here, I'll go somewhere else!'

'How?' he asked. 'I'm not about to hand over the car keys, and we're miles from any other place you might find accommodation.'

'I don't care,' she claimed wildly. 'I'd rather sleep in a barn than with you!'

'Don't be ridiculous.' He was coldly furious now, and making no attempt to conceal it. 'And keep your voice down.'

Desperate for something—anything—that would hurt him the way she was hurting, she aimed the only barb she could find. 'You're not only nearly old enough to be my father, you even sound like one!'

His upper lip curled. 'Perhaps I should try acting like one.' He paused, made a sound of self-disgust. 'Forget it. I'm your husband, not your father. We need to talk this thing through sensibly.'

'We already talked,' she said, voice subdued now. 'You made everything perfectly clear.'

'You wanted honesty, I gave you honesty.' He studied her reflectively for a moment, then sighed, lifting his shoulders in a gesture that could have been construed as apologetic. 'I'm no Prince Charming, Caryn. I never was. But I'm still the same man you were happy to be with and married to until a few short hours ago.'

'No, you're not. You're someone else. Someone I don't want to know,' she ended raggedly.

'Well, that's unfortunate, because you're going to have to get to know me.' He lifted both cases and carried them past her to sling them on to the bed. 'I'd suggest we unpack, and then think about changing for dinner. The jeans might be OK for day-wear, but not for evening.'

I'll wear what I like when I like, she was on the verge of retorting, but she bit it back. He was right up to a point: she had been acting childishly. From now on she would be totally adult about things.

Logan unpacked his own case, stowing both clothing and toilet articles away with speed and precision. Caryn was still only halfway through when he disappeared into the small en-suite bathroom to shower and shave.

She had brought far too many clothes, she knew, but she had visualised being prepared for any eventuality. The two filmy nightdresses and matching négligés she had bought with such dreamy excitement had been pushed away in a drawer before Logan could see them, although, as she had nothing more practical in the way of nightwear with her, she was going to have to wear one or the other, she supposed.

Logan may have won the battle over sharing a room, but he wasn't going to get her into bed with him. There were two deep and comfortable-looking armchairs she could pull together to form a bed of sorts. Adequate for someone her size, at any rate, if not exactly the way she had anticipated spending her wedding-night.

Some honeymoon! she thought corrosively, taking refuge from pain in anger and disgust. Some man she had married who could do this to her! Well, he would learn she was made of stronger stuff than he had believed.

CHAPTER FOUR

LOGAN was wearing a crisp cream-coloured shirt and beige suit trousers when he emerged from the bathroom, much to Caryn's relief. She hadn't seen him take the things in with him, and had half expected him to walk out dressed in nothing more than a towel—or even totally nude.

She had seen a man wholly naked just the once, and that only in a magazine picture glimpsed over a fellow traveller's shoulder on a train. The thought of seeing Logan that way made her heart miss a beat even now. There was no excess fat on him; she knew that already. Just hard muscle and firm flesh. There was hair on his chest; she knew that too, having slipped her fingers inside his shirt when he was kissing her.

He had been so circumspect this past week in his embraces—that alone should have told her something. She doubted now if he really even wanted her physically all that much. He had simply been going through the motions.

'I'll be down in the bar,' he said, pulling on his suit jacket without so much as a glance in her direction. 'I feel in need of a good stiff drink. I ordered dinner for eight-thirty, so don't take too long.'

He was gone before she could find a reply—if any reply had been needed. Caryn stirred herself from the armchair where she had been sitting, and went to select clean underwear from the drawer where she had laid it a bare few minutes ago, along with a dark blue tunic dress from the wardrobe. Her legs had a good enough tan to make tights or stockings inessential on such a warm evening. She rarely wore them in summer, anyway, and saw no reason to change the habit now.

Like the rest of the furnishings, the wardrobe was made of oak, the wood darkened with age and smelling of beeswax. At any other time Caryn would have found the whole room with its cottagey décor and deep dormer windows an absolute delight. At present she couldn't summon the slightest interest.

Showered and dressed, she applied eye-shadow and lipstick with a surprisingly steady hand and ran a brush over her hair. Her face in the mirror looked pale, with faint shadows under the eyes, but she made no attempt to improve her appearance any further. Why bother? she asked herself. She wasn't out to impress anyone, Logan least of all.

He was seated on one of the tall stools at the bar and chatting with the barman when she went down at a quarter-past eight. The bar itself was busy, with every seat occupied and several people standing. Logan rose from the stool when he saw her approaching, and indicated that she should sit down in his place. Caryn did so because it would have looked odd if she stood while he sat. In any case, she doubted if he would have allowed it.

Standing, he towered over her, too close for comfort. Not that he had much choice, she was bound to concede, considering the lack of room. She asked for a Babycham because she couldn't think of anything else on the spur of the moment, and wondered how many whiskies he had consumed in the past twenty minutes or so. Not that he looked in the least bit intoxicated. Stone-cold sober, in fact.

'I hadn't expected quite so many people,' he admitted, glancing round. 'We'd have been better taking a cottage.'

Caryn was glad they hadn't. The last thing she wanted was to be entirely alone with him. At least here there was a certain security to be gained from the fact that the other bedrooms were occupied. Logan wouldn't dare make too much fuss over her refusal to share the bed with him, for fear of people overhearing.

Dinner in the olde-worlde restaurant was excellent, although in her present state of mind, Caryn scarcely felt able to do it justice. She drank two glasses of wine in quick succession, welcoming the heady sensation and confidence-boost as the alcohol content took effect.

Logan made seemingly easy conversation throughout the meal. His whole demeanour was easy, as if nothing that had passed between them these past few hours had touched him. But then it wouldn't have, Caryn told herself. He hadn't had any illusions to be destroyed.

The marriage might be just an expedience, but he meant to make the most of it. He had made that plain enough upstairs. Supposing she put emotion aside and did the same? she speculated, aroused by the wine to a point where none of it seemed quite so important any more.

Regardless of what else he was or wasn't, Logan was still the most vitally male and attractive man she had ever met. He put every other man in the room in the shade. She wasn't the only one who thought so either, to judge from the glances directed his way by one or two other female diners.

If he was aware of the interest, he wasn't revealing it. His attention appeared to be entirely on her. She blossomed beneath it, eyes luminous, mouth curving, skin softly glowing. Every movement of his hands stirred her senses. Such wonderful, masculine, knowledgeable hands. She yearned to feel them on her, holding her, caressing her, making her yield to him. He wanted her that way if no other way. At least right now he did. She could see it in his eyes.

It was gone ten by the time they finished the meal, and darkness was settling in.

'I think we might call it a day,' said Logan softly when they reached the lobby.

Still influenced by the wine, Caryn found little wrong with that suggestion. She was floating on Cloud Nine, seeing the world through rose-coloured spectacles again. Mrs Logan Bannister. Right now it sounded wonderful.

There was enough light left to make switching on a lamp in the bedroom unnecessary for the moment. Logan closed the door and turned her into his arms to kiss her with lingering promise, fingers seeking the zip fastener at her nape. The faint rasp of the teeth seemed to echo in her ears. She quivered afresh to the feel of those sensitive fingertips on her bare skin, tracing the ridge of her spinal column down to the very top of her bikini briefs, then rising again to slip the clip of her brief lacy brassière and seek the firm young curve of her breast.

Involuntarily she arched her back, moaning deep in her throat at the mingled pain and pleasure of his caress. She wanted to be closer, to have that same hand everywhere; to be lifted the way he had lifted her once before and carried to a place where they could lie down together. She remembered as if it were only yesterday, the feel of him inside her—the potent demand of his loins, claiming her for his own. She had been his, and only his, ever since, and always would be. Always, always, always!

As if in direct response to her unspoken plea, he slid an arm under her knees and carried her across to the bed, laying her down on top of the cover and removing her shoes. The darkness had intensified to a point where his eyes looked more black than grey—except for the tiny flame that seemed to flicker in their depths.

He stood up for a moment to remove his jacket, coming back again to take the tunic top and draw it down over her arms. Her brassière went with it, leaving her nude to the waist. Gazing up at him, she saw the light in his eyes glow suddenly fiercer, then his head was descending, his lips closing around one tender nipple, teasing it to aching, tingling prominence in a combination of sucking and nibbling and tongue lapping that drove her wild. She stifled the moans dragged from the very depths of her being with the back of a hand against her lips, writhing against the torment yet wanting it to go on.

It was only when he began easing her dress down over her hips that her mind suddenly snapped back into gear, overcoming the effect of the wine she had drunk. After all he had done, after all she had said, she was giving way to him as if nothing mattered.

But it did matter. This was just sex, not love. If she settled for it, she would be no better than he was.

'Get away from me!' she said through clenched teeth. 'Just get away from me, Logan!'

He went very still, face blanked of all expression, the flame fading from his eyes to leave them dark as night. 'What kind of game do you think you're playing?' he demanded roughly.

'It's no game. Not to me!' She tried to roll away from him, every nerve in her body tensing as he caught her by the shoulders and held her down flat on the bed. 'Take your hands off me!' she spat at him. 'I don't want you touching me!'

'You wanted it a moment ago,' he gritted. 'And more!'

'I had too much wine,' she claimed wildly. 'I didn't know what I was doing.'

'And now you do. Just like that.' There was a grim scepticism in his voice. 'You're not just a liar, you're a poor liar!'

'*You* lied to *me*,' she accused. 'You tricked me into this marriage!'

He gave a sudden heavy sigh, relaxing his grip on her a little. 'Not so much a lie as just not telling you the whole truth. I do care about you, Caryn. I always did.'

But not to the point of loving her the way she wanted to be loved, she thought numbly. The way she had imagined being loved.

'If you do,' she forced out between lips gone stiff as boards, 'you'll leave me alone.'

A muscle jerked in the strong jawline. 'That's putting me in a cleft stick.'

'I don't care.' Caryn was past thinking rationally, intent only on retaliation for the hurt she had suffered and was suffering still. 'Just leave me alone!'

For a moment he made no move at all, then he shrugged abruptly and got to his feet. 'As you prefer.'

Caryn lay in frozen silence as he drew on his jacket again and moved to the door, only now beginning to acknowledge that this wasn't what she wanted at all. She tried to call him back, but the words stuck in her throat. Then it was too late because the door had closed behind him.

Several minutes passed before she finally forced herself to get up. Where Logan had gone, and whether he would be back, she had no idea. She told herself she didn't much care if he never came back. She hated him not only for what he had done, but for what he could still make her feel.

Moving like an automaton, she finished undressing and donned one of the nightdress and négligé sets, resisting any impulse to glance in the full-length cheval mirror as she passed it on the way to the bathroom. It didn't matter what she looked like. Not any more.

She was lying in the bed, face turned to the window, when Logan did return some hour or so later. He neither spoke nor switched on a light, but simply proceeded to get undressed.

Senses heightened, Caryn heard the rattle of loose change as he emptied his pockets, the rasp of a zip, the faint thud of first one shoe and then the other being dropped to the floor. She had seen no pyjamas lying around, and he didn't open a drawer, leaving her to draw the conclusion that he either slept in his underpants, which hardly seemed likely, or wore nothing at all in bed.

The latter notion sent swift heat coursing through her veins. Even if he made no attempt to touch her voluntarily, a double bed was hardly large enough to preclude any possibility of coming into contact during the night. How would he be likely to react if she rolle⁴ over in her sleep—always supposing she managed to sleep?

He returned from the bathroom after five endless minutes, padding across the carpet to slide between the sheets in one smooth movement.

'I know you're not asleep,' he said levelly, 'so we'll get this out of the way here and now. I'll leave you alone, but you have to play your part convincingly enough for my mother to suspect nothing wrong between us. Are you willing to do that?'

Her voice was scarcely audible. 'For her sake ... yes.'

'Fine.' There was a lengthy pause before he added quietly, 'Goodnight.'

Caryn made no reply. What seemed like only bare moments later his breathing deepened and regulated, while she still lay wide awake and heartsick gazing at the patch of star-sprinkled sky revealed by the uncovered window. This should have been the most wonderful night of her life. Instead it was nothing more than a sham. Logan didn't even care enough to find sleep difficult to come by.

They returned to Whitegates in blazing sunshine on the Sunday afternoon, to find Helen Bannister resting on the terrace.

'I wasn't expecting you back until last thing,' she admitted, sitting up with a smile, 'but it's good to have you back. You'd better tell Mrs Lawson you'll be here for dinner, Logan.'

'She knows,' he returned. 'She saw us arrive. Tea's on its way.' He paused, eyes assessing. 'How are you feeling?'

'Fine,' she assured him. Her glance came back to Caryn's face, taking on a slight uncertainty as if she saw something there that didn't quite fit the image. 'You look very brown,' was all she said.

'We did a lot of walking,' Caryn acknowledged, and tried to make her tone as easy as Logan's had been. 'Even part of the Cotswold Way. The scenery round there is so lovely!'

'It's good that you both like the active life.' Helen was smiling again, obviously reassured. 'Opposites may attract, but it's similarities that endure.'

Logan said drily, 'Not always true. You and Dad were totally dissimilar, and you endured.'

His mother laughed. 'There's an exception to every rule. Your father and I learned to cope with our differences.'

'More so than he and I did.'

'Mostly because you'd neither of you ever compromise.' She made a wry gesture. 'Anyway, it's all in the past now. Whitegates is yours to run whichever way you like. Are you still planning on opening a riding school as a sideline?'

'Yes. There's scope for it.'

'Only in summer, surely?' said Caryn, feeling it time she showed some interest. 'I mean, once the holiday season is over, there wouldn't be much of a demand,' she tagged on a little lamely as both mother and son looked at her.

'We're not talking about pony rides on the sands for the kids,' Logan answered pleasantly enough. 'Not everyone can afford to keep their own mount, and true horse-lovers take no account of the season. There's plenty of room for another couple of stable blocks, and an indoor arena for bad weather too.'

'Do you ride yourself?' asked Helen.

Caryn shook her head. 'I could never have afforded lessons, even if there had been a riding stables nearby.'

'Well, there's no reason why you shouldn't learn now. Logan can teach you.'

'By all means.' He sounded amenable, but a faint spark had appeared in the grey eyes. 'As soon as I find a suitable novice's mount.'

Now was not the time, Caryn decided, to state that she didn't particularly like horses. She had never felt an urge to ride, and saw no reason why it should be deemed necessary for her to learn, but that was something to be discussed between her and Logan alone.

Tea was brought out by Mrs Lawson. A cheerful, bustling woman whom Caryn had liked on sight, she ran the house like clockwork and obviously thought the world of her employer. Whether she knew of Mrs Bannister's impending death was difficult to tell, but Caryn doubted it. Apart from her own family, who were sworn to secrecy, no one else was supposed to know. Her mother-in-law had a dread of being pitied.

'I had the bedroom next to yours stripped of its furnishings ready for you to choose your own décor,' said the latter a little later. 'It will make a comfortable sitting-room for the two of you.'

'There's no need for separate quarters,' Logan answered before Caryn could speak.

His mother smiled. 'No need, perhaps, but it's always nice to have somewhere private to retire to on occasion—even if it's only to watch a different programme on television.'

'I'm not going to have much time for television-watching,' he returned, disregarding the gentle teasing note. 'There's a lot of sorting out to do.'

'Not to the extent of neglecting your wife, I hope.' The tone was light but not without significance. 'There's time for everything.'

'I shan't feel neglected, Mrs Bannister.' Caryn did her best to sound undisturbed. 'I'm sure I can find plenty to occupy me.'

The older woman pulled a face. 'I don't expect you to call me Mother, but the Mrs is a little formal. You'd better make it Helen.'

'All right, Helen.' Smile fixed, she got to her feet. 'I think I'll go and unpack, if you don't mind.'

'Don't bother with mine,' said Logan briefly. 'I'll see to it later.'

Caryn refrained from telling him she had no intention of touching his things, contenting herself with a nod.

She had known it would be difficult, she thought wryly, going indoors, but she hadn't realised just how difficult. Helen Bannister had condoned the marriage in the belief that love already existed between her son and his chosen bride, and must go on being convinced of it if she was to have any peace of mind during the coming weeks. She had claimed to be feeling fine, but her appearance belied that statement. Her skin looked almost translucent, the fine boning of her face too clearly defined. If she lasted another six months it would be a miracle.

These last few days had passed more quickly than Caryn had anticipated. There had even been times when memory had taken a back seat. It was the nights that had proved so unbearable. Lying there in the double bed, unable to sleep for hours on end, she had been tempted on more than one occasion to throw the whole thing aside and take whatever Logan was capable of offering her. If he had made any further move himself towards consummating the marriage, she would probably have melted into his arms, but he had stuck to his word. He had all he needed from her; the rest wasn't important enough to waste any sleep over.

All the same, a man of his nature was unlikely to stay celibate for too long, she reflected now. If he couldn't get satisfaction from her, he would surely look elsewhere for it. Which he might well have done in any case, once he had exhausted her potential, she supposed. Once a womaniser always a womaniser.

It was still only just gone five when she finished unpacking. Her mother always served the main meal at lunchtime on a Sunday, and a high tea at six o'clock, which meant she would most probably be taking advantage of the fine weather out in the garden at present. There was a telephone on the bedside table. Sitting on the bed edge, Caryn dialled the number, suddenly aching to hear the familiar voice.

It was her father who answered the call. 'So you're back,' he said a little lamely, as if uncertain of just how to greet her. 'We thought you might decide to take a longer break while the fine weather lasts.'

'Logan had to get back.' Caryn kept her tone light. 'He has a lot of catching up to do. How are you and Mom?'

'Little changed from when you last saw us. It's only been a few days.'

She forced a laugh. 'A lot can happen in a few days.' The hesitation was brief. 'You still haven't forgiven me, have you?'

'Forgive isn't the word,' he said. 'We love you, and we miss you, and we're trying our best to come to terms with losing you to a man we don't even know.'

'You haven't lost me. I'm only just up the road.'

'In miles, perhaps.' His voice briskened. 'When are we going to see you?'

'Tomorrow,' she hazarded. 'I can't walk out on Mrs Bannister tonight after just getting back.' She added quickly, 'How was the dinner party?'

'Excellent, of course, though they're not really our kind of people.'

They most likely wouldn't be her kind of people either, Caryn reflected after ringing off. Not if they were anything like Margot. Hopefully Logan was going to be too busy to think of doing much socialising. She had enough to contend with.

With close on three hours to go before dinner, she could hardly spend them hiding away up here, she decided with reluctance. Logan had given her a guided tour of the farm before the wedding, but she didn't feel up to wandering around on her own as yet. It seemed unlikely that the time would ever come when she could regard Whitegates as home. Best not to, anyway. Once his mother had gone, Logan would no doubt take immediate steps to terminate this fiasco of a marriage.

She found Helen Bannister sitting alone when she finally nerved herself to go down again. Logan had gone to the stables.

'You'll have to get used to not seeing a great deal of him during the daytime,' Helen advised. 'Unless, of course, you start to take an interest yourself.' She added shrewdly, 'I've a feeling you don't care very much for horses at all?'

'I don't know anything about them,' Caryn acknowledged. 'Except that they're very big, and it looks a long way down to the ground.'

'So you have at least been up on a horse?'

'Logan brought me here on horseback that very first time.'

'Of course.' A smile touched the other's lips. 'So romantic!'

Romance hadn't been uppermost in Logan's mind on either occasion he had taken her for a ride, thought Caryn.

'My knight on a white charger!' she agreed with irony. 'Except that it wasn't. White, I mean. But a knight on a brown charger doesn't sound the same.'

Her mother-in-law's gaze sharpened a fraction, as if in recognition of some discordant note. 'Is everything all right between the two of you?' she asked after a moment.

Caryn took a grip on herself. 'Of course. Why?'

'You just seem . . . different, that's all.'

'Well, I suppose I am, a little.' She was choosing her words with care. 'After all, I'm a married woman now.'

'With new responsibilities,' Helen agreed, borrowing her tone. 'You've a dinner invitation for tomorrow evening, by the way. I took the call for you this morning.'

Caryn's smile had faded completely. 'Who from?'

'Margot Ashley. It won't be the only one. A lot of people are going to want to meet you.'

'I'm not all that used to dinner parties.' Caryn tried hard to damp down the panic in her voice. 'I shan't know what to say to anyone.'

'You just have to be yourself. Curiosity will soon die a natural death,' Helen added reassuringly. 'In any case, I doubt very much if Logan will be prepared to accept more than one or two invitations. He was never too keen on the social scene.'

Caryn hoped he still felt the same way. She knew a sudden sharp longing for her former uncomplicated, if admittedly somewhat boring, lifestyle. There might not have been any highs, but neither had there been any real lows, such as the one she was experiencing at present.

'If you don't mind being left to your own devices, I think I'll go and have a lie down for an hour before dinner,' said Helen. 'I'm feeling rather tired.'

'Of course I don't mind,' Caryn assured her swiftly. 'I'll be fine.'

'If you need anything, you only have to ask Mrs Lawson. In fact, it would be a good idea if you started taking over as mistress of the household right away. It doesn't entail so much.' The tone was matter-of-fact. 'I'll see you at dinner.'

Caryn made no reply for the simple reason that she couldn't think of anything to say except thank you, which hardly fitted the occasion. She didn't want to be mistress of the household. Especially not in such circumstances.

Helen had more courage than she would ever have in her position, she thought hollowly. It made her own problems look almost petty by comparison. This marriage might not be all she had dreamed of, but it was all she had, and keeping Logan at arm's length wasn't going to make it any better. She could at least make him want her again if she put her mind to it. That had to be a start.

She stayed out on the terrace until gone seven waiting for Logan to return, only to find him already showered and changed when she finally gave up and went to their room.

'I was beginning to think you'd run home to Mummy,' he said sardonically.

'Are you sure you don't mean hoped?' Caryn flashed, stung by his tone.

'In some respects, it might be best for us both,' he returned. 'Unfortunately, it isn't that simple.'

'I know it.' She was subdued again, wanting to straighten things out between them but not at all sure how to start. 'I wouldn't do anything to upset your mother.'

'That's something, I suppose.' He sounded suddenly weary. 'If you fancy a drink before dinner, come to the library when you're ready.'

Caryn searched her mind for something to say as he moved on past her, but nothing came. It was going to take more than words alone to heal the rift, anyway, she thought wryly. Whether she was capable of a more physical approach, she didn't know. The very fact that Logan had made no further attempt at all to break down the barriers seemed to indicate a total loss of interest in that direction. If he rejected her the way she had rejected him, she would die a thousand deaths!

At seven-thirty, wearing a white pleated skirt and sleeveless tan blouse, she made her way down to the library, to find her mother-in-law there but no Logan.

'He's making a call in the study,' Helen informed her in answer to the unspoken question. 'Come and sit by me, dear. Logan will get you a drink when he comes back.'

Seated there in the golden glow of the evening sunlight, Caryn felt so utterly out of place. Like all the others in the house, this was a beautiful and gracious room, but the book-lined walls seemed to be closing in on her—trapping her in a world she neither knew nor cared about. When Logan put in an appearance it was even worse. The two of them were a family, she the interloper.

About to plump for a safe sherry when he asked her what she wanted to drink, she knew a sudden urge to kick over the traces, if only for show. 'Gin and tonic, please,' she said firmly, and saw a hint of irony in the grey eyes.

'Ice and lemon?'

'Please,' she said again.

With little experience of spirits, she found the drink far from palatable. It had been a silly gesture, in any case, she acknowledged ruefully after just one sip. Logan was by no means impressed.

'You spoke to Margot?' asked Helen as her son poured himself a drink.

'Yes,' he acknowledged. 'It seems she wanted to make sure she was the first to offer hospitality—although from the sound of it, everyone else will be there too.' He dropped into a chair opposite the sofa Caryn was sharing with his mother, grey eyes enigmatic as they rested on her face. 'We've been invited out to dinner tomorrow evening.'

'Yes,' Caryn answered, 'I know.' Hardly knowing what else to say, she took another sip from her glass, trying not to grimace. 'Will it be a dressy occasion?'

'Black tie. Margot always did believe in doing things in style.' His tone was dry. 'Short notice, but it's as well to get it over with.'

'I heard a rumour that she and Duncan are on the verge of splitting up?' said his mother. 'A pity, of course, if they do, although they were never really suited, I always thought.'

'Rumour has a way of becoming exaggerated in the telling,' came the level response. 'They're just going through a bad patch, that's all.'

If he knew that much about it, who had told him? Caryn wondered. Duncan—or Margot herself? At least the Ashleys' marriage had lasted a while before going through a bad patch. Their own had begun with one.

CHAPTER FIVE

FAMILY dinner at Whitegates was no formal affair, but it was still very different from what Caryn had been accustomed to at home. Her mother rarely bothered to set the table in the small dining-room, preferring to eat in the kitchen. Caryn had thought nothing of it until now. Faced with gleaming silver and sparkling crystal and the warm glow of lovingly polished mahogany, she was bound to concede that genteel living had its points.

She contributed little to the general conversation over the following hour or so, not because she was tongue-tied but because most of the talk was centred around farm business. The way to most men's hearts might be through the stomach, she reflected, but where Logan was concerned horses obviously took precedence over food any day of the week. Her lack of experience with or interest in the animals was one more nail in the coffin so far as a successful marriage went.

Interest could be taken and experience gained, of course. The question was, did she want to make that effort in light of what she knew? Regardless of his protestations, Logan didn't love her. She had, as he had admitted, been the only choice. What he really meant was that she had been the only one gullible enough to take his haste to be married at face value.

Helen retired for the night at ten o'clock. As soon as she was gone, Logan announced his intention of making a last round of the stables. He didn't suggest that Caryn go with him, and she wasn't about to offer her company.

Left alone in the drawing-room, she flicked through a magazine or two, but her mind wasn't on what she was looking at. Logan hadn't needed to check up, she was sure. There was a night guard on duty. Over-zealousness, she wondered, or simply a need for a little solitude?

Her despondency deepened. They couldn't go on like this. It was an impossible situation. Yet what to do about it? If she took steps to renew their physical relationship she was in effect saying that the rest didn't matter. She wanted love, not just sexual satisfaction.

She was in bed, though far from sleep, when he eventually came up. He followed a ritual that had become familiar over these past few nights, first undressing then disappearing into the bathroom, to emerge some ten minutes later showered and smelling faintly of minted toothpaste.

So far she had managed to stay on her own side of the bed, and with her back to him, and in the mornings he was always up before she awoke, so she still wasn't sure if he wore anything. Tonight, as on the other nights, she lay rigid as he slid between the sheets, wanting so badly to turn to him yet unable to conquer her pride. If he wanted her he would surely make some move.

It was the silence that got too much for her in the end. He wasn't asleep; she could tell that from his breathing.

'It's a pity you didn't know about Margot's marriage breaking up,' she said bitingly. 'You could have taken up where you left off!'

The response was so long in coming that she was beginning to think he must be asleep after all. When he did speak it was without particular inflection. 'What makes you think I might have wanted to?'

'Everything.'

'Such as?' he insisted.

'Such as the fact that you're so eager to see her again, short notice or not.'

'There's going to be more than one person there tomorrow night,' he reminded her, still in the same un-emotional tones. 'I've known Duncan many years.'

'The man she put in your place.'

'Not so. As I've told you before, there was never any arrangement between us.'

'*She* obviously thought there was.'

'Then she was wrong. And to answer your other suggestion, while divorce might be a lot easier than it used to be, it could hardly have been soon enough for my needs.'

'If divorce is so easy, there's nothing to stop you div-orcing me now that you've got what you want,' Caryn retorted, allowing bitterness full rein. 'I wouldn't fight it.'

'Unfortunately it's still necessary to wait rather longer than a few days before application, so I'd forget it for the time being.' There was more than a hint of weariness now. 'Just go to sleep.'

'Oh, sure! Just go to sleep like a good little girl!' She was too incensed to care how irrational she was being. 'In case you'd forgotten, I stopped being a good little girl two years ago!'

He didn't move, but the tension in the air was almost tangible. 'Are you trying to provoke me into something, by any chance?' he asked with dangerous softness.

Caryn swallowed on the sudden dryness in her throat. *Was* that what she was doing?

'Don't be ridiculous,' she got out.

The hand on her shoulder pulled her over on to her back, holding her there with a purpose that made every nerve-ending in her body tremor. Logan had raised himself on an elbow, eyes glittering, bare shoulders gleaming like oiled silk in the shaft of moonlight from the window behind him. His legs were bare too; she could feel the hard warmth of his thigh through the material of her nightdress.

'Is this what you're after?' he said, and brought his head down to find her mouth.

The kiss was far from gentle, yet it stirred some deep-down part of her that she hadn't wanted to acknowledge. She made some attempt at resistance, but it was only a token gesture. Her whole body yearned for the touch of his hands, for the masculine assertion she had known from him in the past, breaking down the barriers pride alone had erected against him. Love her or not, she wanted him.

His anger was transmuted into passion of a different kind as she began to answer the demand in his lips. The hand he sent searching the length of her leg beneath her nightdress was sensitive to every nerve and pulse-beat, fingers so light and yet so utterly in command.

She quivered all over as he caressed the smoothness of her thigh, moving in slow circles that almost but never quite reached the cluster of blonde curls—rousing her to a point where she could barely contain the aching desire.

But he wasn't ready yet to grant her that release. Still kissing her, he moved his hand up over her stomach, fingers splaying now to encompass the fluttering muscles for a brief moment before carrying on their exploration, following the curve of her hip and waist to reach her breast, not gentle, not rough but somewhere wonderfully and rightly in between.

Caryn caught her breath as pleasure flooded her. There was no thought now of anything but what Logan was doing to her. Dear, dominant Logan; the only man who had ever touched her this way; the only man she had ever wanted to touch her this way!

'You don't need this,' he said in low and roughened tones as he slid the thin straps of her nightdress over her arms and peeled it down the length of her body. 'I want to see you—feel you against me.'

He put the lips to her breast, running his tongue over and around her peaking, throbbing nipple, dragging an involuntary cry from her lips. She clutched wildly at the dark head, hardly knowing what she was doing in the sheer sensory excitation, feeling the crisp thickness of his hair between her fingers.

She became fully aware of his nudity as he shifted his body into closer contact—the potent evidence of his arousal pressing against her thighs. But only for a moment or two before he levered himself away from her again, tossing back the covering sheet to expose her whole body to the moonlight, eyes devouring her. Caryn fought the childish urge to cover herself with her hands. Logan had every right to look at her this way, every right to know her in intimate detail. All the same, she stiffened up a little when he began a more physical exploration.

'Relax,' he said softly. 'I won't hurt you. You're so smooth and firm, my darling. Utterly beautiful!'

My darling. The endearment was enough on its own to ease away the last of her reticence, even though a part of her knew that it meant little in reality. Heart thudding, senses swirling, she gave herself fully into his hands: such wonderfully possessive hands. His mouth was an even greater source of pleasure, making her gasp and writhe in an ecstasy of sensation.

When he finally came over her, she was avid for the feel of him inside her, the pulsing incursion she remembered so well. Only this time there was no pain, only pure exhilaration, no fear to come because Logan was her husband now and it no longer mattered if she got pregnant.

She wanted to be pregnant. If she had his child, perhaps he would love her then.

It was daylight when she awoke, and for a moment her mind remained blank. The realisation that she was nude brought memory back with a rush, along with a sudden wave of heat. Had that wanton creature last night really been her? She could scarcely credit it.

She forced herself to turn over, torn between relief and disappointment to find the other side of the bed empty. It was only a little after seven, she saw from the bedside clock. From the lack of body warmth on Logan's side of the bed she deduced that he must have been up for some time. No doubt he would be down at the stables by now.

She had gone to sleep with his arms about her last night, and would have been a great deal happier to have woken this morning in the same state. Just how much, she wondered, had last night meant to him, that he could simply up and leave her like this?

The answer was only too achingly obvious. No more than any other passionate episode. Only husbands in love with their wives bothered to kiss them awake in the mornings—unless, of course, they were seeking further satisfaction. Apparently Logan hadn't even been interested in repeating the experience.

There had been no attempt on his part to use any form
of protection, she recalled, so unless he was taking it for
granted that she was on the Pill he wasn't averse to
getting her pregnant. He might already have accomplished it, in fact. Perhaps it was what he really
wanted.

Dressed in jeans and gingham shirt, she went tentatively down to the smaller breakfast-room at eight
o'clock, to find Helen Bannister seated alone.

'Logan will be down at the stables,' she said, accu-
rately guessing Caryn's unspoken question. 'He'll have
eaten breakfast already.' Her smile was teasing. 'You
must have been very deeply asleep not to hear him go.'

Caryn kept her voice light. 'I must have been.'

'So what plans do you have for today?' Helen continued as she took her place at the table and reached for
the coffee-pot. 'Logan will be tied up, I'm afraid. He
has a lot of restructuring to do.'

'I thought I might visit my parents,' Caryn acknowledged. 'I know it's only been a few days since I saw
them, but...' She paused, gave an apologetic little shrug.
'Well, it still feels strange to be here instead of there.'

'Of course it does.' Helen sounded unperturbed. 'It's
nice that your parents live so near. You'll be able to pop
over any time you feel like it. You do drive?'

'Well, yes.'

'Good. You can use my Rover. It's been stuck in the
garage for the last two months since I gave up driving
myself. In fact there's no reason why we shouldn't have
it transferred to your name. I shan't be using it again.'

There was no element of self-pity in her voice; she was
simply stating a fact. Her mother-in-law had to be the
bravest woman she had ever met, thought Caryn, trying
not to show any emotion herself. Reluctant though she

was to accept such an offer, refusing it would be like throwing generosity in her face.

'Thank you,' she said steadily.

'Thank *you*,' came the equally steady reply. 'Logan made a good choice.'

Logan made the only choice, Caryn could have replied, but refrained. Helen already knew the reason for her son's marriage. What she must *not* know was just how much was lacking from it.

'If this dinner party tonight is really going to be a dressy affair, what kind of thing should I wear?' she asked by way of changing the subject.

'Oh, a cocktail dress will be quite suitable. Few wear long these days, unless it's a very special event.'

Caryn bit her lip. 'I doubt if anything I have would do. Most of my clothes are separates, so that I can ring the changes.'

'You can always drive into Norwich and buy a dress,' Helen suggested, showing no concern. 'I can tell you where to find the shop I use myself on occasion. They'd be sure to have what you need.'

'How much would it be likely to cost?' asked Caryn diffidently.

'That's the last thing you need concern yourself over. Just tell them who you are, and they'll send the bill. Better still, I'll ring through and tell them you're coming. It might be best to make it this morning rather than leave it until afternoon. You don't want to be cutting it too fine.'

As Logan's wife, with no income of her own and precious little savings, Caryn expected it was only right and proper that he should pay for any clothes she needed, but she still felt reluctant to take advantage, especially without his knowledge.

'Logan must see about making you a proper allowance,' Helen said now on a practical note. 'I'll have a word with him.'

'I'd rather you didn't,' Caryn responded, and drew a look of surprise.

'It's the normal course, my dear. I'm sure Logan would have already arranged it if he didn't have so much on his mind just now. No wife should be in the position of having to ask her husband for money to spend on personal things. It's his place to provide the wherewithal—just as it's his place to take care of all the other expenses.'

Caryn had to smile. 'We come from different worlds. My father never made enough to give Mom any kind of personal allowance. Not that she ever really wanted for anything,' she added swiftly. 'Neither did I.'

'I'm sure you didn't. Your father strikes me as a very responsible man. But you have to accustom yourself to our way of life now.' The older woman's voice briskened. 'I told Mrs Lawson you'd eat a full breakfast. I hope I did right?'

She was certainly hungry enough, Caryn conceded, making the appropriate reply. Faced with the dilemma of what to wear tonight, and with Logan not here to give the go ahead himself, she could do no other but follow Helen's advice and make the trip into Norwich.

It was necessary to change from her jeans into something a little less casual before doing so, though. Standing before the wardrobe in briefs and bra, trying to choose something suitable, she was taken totally by surprise when Logan came into the room.

'My riding boot split,' he said. 'I need my spare pair.' He lifted a sardonic eyebrow as he registered her pink cheeks and general confusion. 'Why the blushes? I've seen you in a great deal less.'

'I wasn't expecting you back,' she said, struggling to overcome her ridiculous embarrassment. 'I don't have anything to wear tonight, so your mother suggested I go into Norwich and buy something.'

'Not like that, I hope.'

'I was just about to put a dress on,' she retorted stiffly, and bit her lip as the sardonicism increased.

'That's a relief.'

'Then it's all right?' Caryn persisted as he moved to his own section of wardrobes. 'My buying a new dress, I mean. I doubt if I have enough money of my own for the kind your mother was talking about.'

'You don't have to ask, for God's sake,' he said brusquely. 'I already opened an account for you at the bank. You buy what you want, when you want.'

'I wasn't to know that,' she defended. 'And I'm not in the habit of taking things for granted.'

Logan straightened up, the boots in his hand, face un-revealing. 'No, of course you're not. I should have told you. Your cheque-book is on the dressing-table, along with your bank card. I've applied for a gold card for you in addition.'

'You're very...generous.' Caryn scarcely knew what else to say. If theirs had been a normal relationship she might have gone to him and shown her appreciation in more tactile fashion, but it wasn't, and she couldn't bring herself to make such a move.

His lips twisted. 'Most women would take it as their right.'

'Only the kind you're used to.'

'True. It never occurred to me before that there was any other kind.'

'Then it's high time you did.' This time there was a sharpness in her voice. 'Why are you being like this, Logan? After last night...' She broke off, colour flooding her face again at the look in the grey eyes.

'Last night you wanted sex and you got sex,' he declared flatly. 'There's every chance we'll be repeating the event, only don't confuse it with anything else. You're no more in love with me now than you were two years ago.'

Pride brought the words to her lips. 'That makes two of us, then!'

The dark head inclined. 'So it appears. But there are compensations. Once you've learned how to give as well as take, you'll be worth staying home for.'

'What's that supposed to mean?' she asked thickly.

'Exactly what it says. You respond but you don't reciprocate. There's a subtle difference.'

The hurt of it was like an iron band about her chest. She took refuge in sarcasm. 'I'm so sorry I failed to match up to what you're used to. Perhaps I should ask Margot for advice.'

'She wouldn't know what the problem was.' He sounded totally unmoved. 'Lovemaking is a two-way affair—or should be. A man finds pleasure in the feel of a woman's hands and lips on his body too.'

Caryn gazed at him in silence, feeling the sudden tension in her stomach muscles. His expression altered as he looked back at her, taking on a wry quality.

'Maybe I'm expecting too much too soon. Enjoy your shopping trip.'

She watched him out of the door, heart heavy. Having read a sex manual belonging to a friend, she wasn't entirely unaware of what he was talking about: men had erogenous zones too. Last night she had wanted to ex-

plore him the way he had explored her, to know every
detail of that wonderful, muscular, masculine body.
What she had lacked was the confidence to let instinct
be her guide.

If she couldn't make him love her, she could at least
learn how to keep him physically interested, she told
herself resolutely. Regardless of what might be missing
from their relationship, she couldn't contemplate being
parted from him now.

The skies were clouded over again today for the first
time in almost a week, although rain wasn't forecast.
Helen had had Bill Lawson fetch the car out on to the
drive for her. No more than a year old, and the largest
of the Rover models, it was twice the size and heaven
only knew how many more times the value of her father's
Renault, which was the only other car Caryn had ever
driven. An automatic too, she noted in dismay, on taking
her seat. What did one do without a gear box and clutch?

What one did, she soon found, was to just sit there
and drive, one foot comfortably at rest and both hands
always on the wheel. The car was top of the range, with
every conceivable luxury. Caryn could hardly believe it
was to be her very own. Not that she wouldn't infinitely
prefer her mother-in-law to be in a fit state to drive it
herself, of course. That went without saying.

Norwich was busy. She crossed the river at Foundry
Bridge and found space in the car park off Market
Avenue below the Castle. Following the directions sup-
plied by her mother-in-law, she reached the narrow street
where the shop she wanted was situated within a few
minutes.

It proved to be a small, bow-windowed establishment
with the name 'Marcelle' on a swinging sign above the

door. Exclusive and expensive, was Caryn's immediate summing up.

Feeling self-conscious in her neat but inexpensive little suit, she went on in, unsurprised to note the somewhat supercilious expression on the face of the elegantly dressed woman who appeared from the rear premises in answer to the discreet tinkle of the door chimes.

'I believe Mrs Bannister rang through to say I would be coming in,' she said quickly, and saw the other undergo a rapid change of attitude.

'Of course! A cocktail dress, isn't it?' She ran an experienced eye over Caryn's slender curves. 'Size ten, I think.' Her lips pursed. 'I'm afraid I don't have too much choice. Most of my clientele are size fourteen and upwards. However, I'm sure I can find you something suitable.'

Gazing at her reflection in the dressing-room mirror some minutes later, Caryn wasn't at all sure. Cut from ivory brocade, the dress was sleeveless, semi-fitted and well below knee-length, the neckline slightly scooped to reveal a discreet expanse of smoothly tanned skin. There were shoes in a pearly ivory leather to go with it, together with a matching clutch bag large enough to hold a handkerchief and lipstick, if precious little else. All very tasteful and classy, but was it really her? She was eighteen, not thirty, for heaven's sake!

No price had been mentioned, and Caryn didn't dare ask. Neither did she have the courage to say what was on her mind. Marcelle had nothing else in her size, so it was this or nothing.

With everything packed away in impressive gold and black boxes, she made her way back to the car. Tonight was going to be an ordeal in more ways than the one, she acknowledged wryly, stowing the boxes away in the

boot. That dress was going to steal what little she had
left of her own identity. She had brought the cheque-
book with her. If she had any guts at all, she would head
for the nearest boutique and buy something more in
keeping with the image she had of herself.

Only she wouldn't, because she hadn't. She would
conform to what was expected of her. Why else would
Mrs Bannister have sent her to such a place if it wasn't
because she considered her dress sense less than adequate to the occasion?

Catching a glimpse of herself in the car window as
she came round to the front, it occurred to her that she
ought to get her hair done too. There shouldn't be too
much difficulty in finding a salon able to take her without
an appointment on a Monday morning.

She was successful at the second attempt, though only
because of a cancellation, she was told by the receptionist. The stylist was male, and totally disapproved of
her present style, which he said did absolutely nothing
for her.

Somewhat tentatively, Caryn allowed him to have his
way, scarcely recognising herself when she saw the finished result. With her hair blow-dried and brushed back
from her face in layered thickness, her cheekbones
seemed so much more prominent, her eyes more widely
spaced.

'Definitely you,' proclaimed her mentor with a
flourish.

Less girlish, at any rate, she thought, looking for some
further assurance. That had to be a plus.

Short of cash as she was, she had no choice but to
use the cheque-book to pay the exorbitant bill. She had
never had a personal current account before, preferring
to draw money from her meagre savings as and when

required. Logan hadn't said how much he had credited to her account, but she would obviously have to know the figure some time in order to budget her expenditure, she reflected. Perhaps it would be easiest to ask the bank for a balance statement.

Logan. The mere thought of him made her pulses leap. Whatever else might be missing, his lovemaking left nothing to be desired. Tonight, she vowed, she would give her instincts free rein. Tonight she would be everything he wanted in a woman. If she could satisfy him that way, he wouldn't need anyone else.

CHAPTER SIX

HAVING called in on her parents, it was mid-afternoon when Caryn finally got back to Whitegates. Her mother-in-law, Mrs Lawson informed her, was resting in her room.

The housekeeper had to realise that something was seriously amiss with her employer, Caryn reflected, taking her packages upstairs. Women Helen's age didn't normally feel the need of rest in the afternoons. If only something could be done to stay the progression of the disease. Some things money obviously couldn't buy.

She liked the dress no better when she saw it again. At least, not for herself. Like it or not, though, she would have to wear it. Nothing else she owned would do.

It needed more than an hour until teatime, when her mother-in-law might put in an appearance again. In the meantime, what did she do with herself? Having the freedom to please oneself was great in theory, but in practice it wasn't all that marvellous. Mrs Lawson, in conjunction with a daily domestic help, kept the household running smoothly, leaving Helen herself with little more than the menus to see to.

There was a whole library full of books waiting to be read, but, much as Caryn loved reading, she wasn't in the mood for it right now. What she needed, she told herself, was some objective in life. Even though she had often found her job boring, it had at least given her some sense of purpose. Perhaps Logan could find her something to do down at the stables. Those riding lessons, for instance. It would be one way of getting closer to him.

Wearing jeans and T-shirt again, she made her way out from the rear of the house to cut down through the gardens. The skies were almost clear now, giving promise of a fine evening to come. They were due at the Ashleys' at eight for eight-thirty. How long the dinner party might go on for, Caryn had no idea. *Too* long for her, without a doubt. She wished it were tomorrow, and all over.

Logan was out riding, she was advised by one of the stable hands on arrival. He should be back any time, he added, if she wanted to wait.

Most of the Whitegates stock was out to grass at present. Caryn wandered down to the near pasture to lean on the gate and view the grazing animals, admiring the glossy hides and general conformation. Even knowing as little about horses as she did, it was easy to see that these particular specimens were thoroughbreds.

There was a foal over in the far corner, she realised as a head was suddenly lifted from the grass. She watched in delight as the youngster hoisted itself to its feet, long legs out of all proportion to its body size, chestnut coat glinting in the sunlight. It was joined by another that had also been lying in the longer grass: black this time, with a white blaze down the centre of its forehead.

The latter kicked up its heels exuberantly and ran in Caryn's direction, pulling up short before it reached the gate to eye her with curiosity. She held out an inviting hand and made coaxing noises, but to no avail, although the little animal showed no sign of nervousness.

On impulse, she unlatched the gate and slipped through. The foal stood its ground as she moved slowly towards it, listening to her low, soothing voice with pricked ears. He jerked his head as she reached out to

stroke the soft nose, but suffered her to touch him,
stretching his neck to nuzzle the waistband of her jeans
in return.

Laughing, totally captivated, Caryn was unaware of
the larger animal moving slowly but surely towards them;
it was the thunder of hoofs from another direction
altogether that alerted her. The big black horse rapidly
approaching looked anything but friendly. He would be
on her before she could open the gate again, Caryn
realised, rooted to the ground in sudden fear.

'Don't just stand there!' clipped a voice from her rear.
'Move!'

Galvanised into action by the very quality of the
command, she turned and ran blindly for the gate being
held open for her by Logan. He slammed it shut again
as the black horse skidded to a halt.

'No harm done,' he said to the animal in conciliatory
tones. 'Calm down!'

Snorting, nostrils flaring, the stallion took a dis-
dainful kick at the gate before moving off. The foal was
suckling from its mother, while the other mares grazed
on unconcernedly.

'Don't you have any more sense than to go into a field
with a stallion and mares at this time of year?' demanded Logan harshly, turning back to Caryn.

Shaken, she gazed at him in mounting anger. 'How
was I supposed to know there was a stallion in the field?'

His lip curled. 'You mean you can't recognise the male
of the species when you see one?'

'*If* I'd seen it. He was right up at the top end.' She
added tautly, 'And if he's so dangerous, you should have
a warning notice!'

'He isn't normally. Not with people he knows and trusts. He just doesn't like strangers messing around with his brood.'

'In other words, I shouldn't even be here without supervision. Isn't that what you're saying?'

The lean features showed no sign of discomfiture. 'It might be advisable. You've no understanding of horses.'

Caryn strove to control herself, aware that he had a valid point. 'Only because I never had the opportunity to be involved with them before.'

Logan studied her for a moment, the line between his brows slowly clearing. 'Do you want to be involved?'

'Yes.' She was eager to convince him. 'Learning to ride would be a start, wouldn't it?'

'It would,' he agreed. 'Unfortunately, we don't have a suitable mount available at present.'

'What about the horse you've just been out on?'

'Dancer?' His lips stretched in a brief smile. 'Think you could handle another stallion?'

Caryn smiled back, glad to be on level footing again. 'Obviously not. I didn't even realise they could be ridden. Aren't they very difficult to control?'

'Only if there's a mare in season around. That foal's dam just came back on heat, which is why Oberon is so touchy.' There was an edge of cynicism to his voice. 'How did the shopping trip go?'

'All right.' Caryn was reluctant to admit the truth. 'Your mother told me where to go for a suitable dress for tonight.'

'She did?' Logan sounded surprised. 'I shouldn't have thought the kind of place she uses would cater for younger tastes.' He slid a casual arm about her shoulders, turning her in the direction of the stable blocks. 'Come and say hello to Dancer, anyway.'

Happy just to be in contact with him again, she went without protest. The arm rested lightly but still felt heart-warmingly protective. She could feel the hardness of his chest against her upper arm, the warmth radiating through the material of his shirt. He looked so utterly and excitingly masculine in the well-fitting jodhpurs and riding boots—so much the man in command. She could hardly wait to be closer still to him, to have him inside her, possessing her, the way he had done last night.

Dancer was a grey, intimidating in his size alone as he stuck a head from his stall in answer to Logan's call. Not caring for the gleam in the animal's eye, Caryn extended a cautious hand to stroke his muzzle.

'He doesn't bite,' said Logan reassuringly, spoiling it by adding, 'Not unless he's provoked.' He shook his head as she hastily withdrew the hand. 'You'll get nowhere by showing fear. Animals can sense it and it makes them nervous too. Talk to him. Let him get to know your voice as well as your scent.'

'Hello, Dancer,' she said, feeling self-conscious. 'Who's a pretty boy, then?'

Logan made a derisive sound. 'He's not a parrot!' He rubbed between the pricked ears, speaking softly. 'We all have our pride, don't we, boy?'

The stallion snickered as if in agreement, obviously recognising real affection. Could she really be feeling jealous of an animal? Caryn asked herself wryly.

'Are you coming back for tea?' she said. 'It's almost time.'

Logan shook his head. 'Not today. You go and keep my mother company.'

She didn't want to leave him, but could find no excuse to stay. 'So what time will you be coming up?'

'I shan't forget we're going out.' He gave the stallion a final pat and turned away, face suddenly devoid of expression. 'We don't need to leave until eight. Elmtree is only ten minutes away.'

Going back alone to the house, Caryn did her level best to achieve a positive outlook. Tonight she would need to show an assured front. Whatever the circumstances, Logan was *her* husband, and Margot had to know it!

She found Helen on the terrace, with the tea-trolley already arrived.

'I was beginning to think I'd have to drink it alone,' the latter commented lightly. 'Did you find a dress?'

'Yes, thanks,' Caryn answered, taking one of the cushioned chairs. She added swiftly, 'You must let me know how much it came to when the account comes through. Logan already arranged an allowance for me.'

'I'm glad to hear it.' Helen gave her a shrewd glance. 'You're not looking forward to this evening, are you?'

Caryn had to be honest about it. 'No,' she admitted. 'It isn't the kind of affair I'm used to.'

'I don't see why that should matter so much. You're an extremely attractive and intelligent young woman, capable, I'm sure, of holding your own in any company.'

'But I *am* likely to be the youngest person there?'

'Well, yes, I suppose you may be, but that should be a plus not a minus point.' Helen laughed. 'You'll be the envy of all the other women!'

Hardly an ideal situation, thought Caryn wryly. In any case, she doubted if it were true. The women in Margot Ashley's circle would be too poised and sophisticated to hanker after being eighteen again.

Logan still wasn't back at seven when she went to start getting ready. Showered, she put on fresh underwear and the gossamer-fine tights Marcelle had also provided, then donned a light cotton wrap while she applied make-up.

Cut and shaped by an expert, her hair needed little attention. Logan hadn't even noticed, she thought dejectedly, viewing the finished image in the mirror. That dress wasn't going to enhance her appearance, although it at least looked fittingly expensive.

She was doing her nails when Logan finally returned.

'We had an emergency,' he said. 'One of the mares went down with colic.'

'Is she going to be all right?' Caryn asked.

'She is now, although it was touch and go for a while. If the bowel twists there's little anyone can do.' He was stripping off his shirt as he spoke. 'I gather you're through with the bathroom?'

Wasn't it obvious? Caryn wondered, taking another swift glance at her reflection.

It was apparently a rhetorical question, because he didn't wait for an answer. 'I like the new hairstyle, by the way,' he said at the door.

Pleasure at the compliment was muted by the thought that he couldn't have been overly impressed with her old style. She wondered if he would like the overall picture she was going to present. He had never made any comment on what she wore to date—apart from their wedding-day when he had told her she looked lovely. But then he would hardly have said anything derogatory, even if he had thought it, would he?

He was wearing nothing but a towel slung about his hips when he emerged from the bathroom not ten minutes later. Extracting clean underpants from his tallboy, he dropped the towel without self-consciousness to pull them on.

Caryn watched him through the mirror, unable to tear her eyes away from the leanly muscled, superbly fit body. Apart from the narrowest of strips about his hips, he was tanned all over to a golden brown. The hair on his chest was wiry, as she already knew by touch: her breasts tingled at the memory of how it felt to be held close against him. Unlike so many men around his age, there was no sign of thickening about his waist, no sagging of stomach muscle.

He looked up suddenly, catching her eye before she could glance away. She felt the hot colour flood her cheeks as one dark brow lifted in sardonic acknowledgement.

'Later,' he said.

The heat in her face increased. 'I wasn't thinking . . . that,' she denied.

'Yes, you were. It was coming across loud and clear.' He pulled on a pristine white evening shirt, his smile lightly mocking. 'Don't look so horror-struck. It's a perfectly natural occurrence. You're a sensual young woman. You always were. That's a plus for any husband. This just isn't the moment.'

'Oh, no, of course!' Anger gave her voice strength. 'You can't possibly be late for Murgot!'

For a brief moment something flared in the grey eyes, then he shrugged. 'I'm not in the habit of being late for anything if I can help it. It might be an idea if you finished getting ready yourself.'

Legs trembling, Caryn forced herself to get to her feet. She no longer cared about the dress, or what Logan might think of it; she didn't care about *him* any more. He was cruel and heartless and he didn't merit any concern on her part.

He had turned away now to pull on black evening trousers. Caryn took off the cotton wrap and seized the dress from its hanger, drawing down the long back zip to slide into it hip-first rather than put it over her head. She stepped into the high-heeled shoes before reaching behind her to pull up the zip again, tugging viciously when the latter stuck at waist level, but to no avail.

'You'll break the teeth if you're not careful,' said Logan, coming up behind her. 'Let me see to it.'

'I can manage!' she said through clenched teeth of her own, and heard his impatiently indrawn breath.

'Don't be silly. The material is caught up. All you're doing is making things worse.'

He was speaking sense, Caryn was bound to acknowledge. There was no way she was going to free the zip without being able to see where the problem lay. She stood rigidly as he went to work, flinching from the touch of his fingers on her bare skin. He was close enough for her to feel the warmth of his breath between her shoulderblades, and catch the subtle scent of aftershave. There was gooseflesh on her arms, an undeniable ache in the pit of her stomach.

She couldn't help feeling this way, she told herself defensively. It was something apart. At the moment she hated him, but her body refused to recognise the emotion.

'There,' he said, and ran the freed zip all the way up. His hand seemed to linger for a moment at her nape, then it was withdrawn and he was moving away again, leaving her standing there yearning for contact of any kind rather than none at all.

Warm as the evening had turned out to be, she could still do with something to put around her shoulders for the journey, she realised, taking a look in the cheval mirror. She did have a black mock silk jacket that might suffice. The neckline needed something to enhance it too, but all she had was a few pieces of costume jewellery, none of which was even remotely suitable.

Logan finished tying his tie and picked up the dinner jacket he had laid ready on the bed. Caryn turned with reluctance to face him as he shrugged into it, registering with fatalistic acceptance the expression that fleetingly crossed his face as he viewed her. She was grateful that he made no comment. A compliment would have been adding insult to injury.

'Ready to go?' he asked.

'I just need a jacket,' she said.

They descended the stairs together but in silence. Caryn wished she only had the courage to back out of going to the dinner party at all. Last night she had believed everything was beginning to come right, but it wasn't, and probably never would. Logan needed the kind of wife she didn't know how to be.

'I have something for you,' he said unexpectedly as they reached the hall. 'Come into the study.'

She accompanied him uncertainly, hovering just inside the door as he crossed the room to swing aside a painting on the wall and reveal what looked like a small safe. A few decisive turns of the combination wheel in the centre brought it open. Logan took a long flat case from within, and shut the door again, spinning the wheel to lock it and replacing the concealing picture before moving to the large mahogany desk under the window.

'Come over here,' he invited.

Caryn did so, eyes widening as he opened the case and took out a double string of creamy pearls.

'A belated wedding present,' he said with a faint twist of his lips. 'I was going to give them to you on the evening itself, but I couldn't find the right moment.'

'I'm...sorry.' It was all she could find to say.

'So am I,' he agreed drily. 'Turn around.'

Biting her lip, she obeyed, wishing there were some way of turning back the clock. If Margot hadn't told her the reason behind Logan's haste to be married, it could all have been so different. What the heart didn't know it didn't pine for.

The pearls settled into the hollow of her throat, taking on almost immediate warmth from her skin. They were real; even she could tell that much. They must, she knew, have cost the earth!

'Thank you,' she got out. 'They feel wonderful!'

'You're welcome.' His fingers moved from her nape to lightly circle her throat just above where the pearls rested. 'You have a lovely neck—a lovely body altogether. The next time you go shopping, make your own choice.'

Throat tight, she said huskily, 'I know I look a mess, but...'

'I didn't say you looked a mess,' he interrupted. 'You couldn't. There's nothing wrong with the dress itself, it's simply not your style. I hate to see women over thirty in short skirts, but you have the youth *and* the legs for them. Be yourself, not what you think others might want you to be.'

'I'll try.' Right at this moment she wanted nothing more than to turn into his arms, but she couldn't bring herself to make the move. If only he would do it for her!

He didn't. Letting her go, he said flatly. 'There are earrings in the box too. Put them on, we're going to be late.'

Elmtree was smaller than Whitegates, though not by so much. The last of the dozen guests to arrive, they were the centre of attention the moment they were ushered inside. Margot looked stunning as always in a black silk catsuit with a plunging neckline and a silver belt. She gave Caryn a fleeting appraisal and dismissed her out of hand, concentrating her attention on Logan in a way that left little doubt, in Caryn's mind at least, of where her main interests lay.

If her husband recognised it too, he gave no sign. Shorter than Logan by a couple of inches, he also looked several years older, probably due to the receding fair hair. Caryn had exchanged no more than a few words with him at the wedding, but had liked him on sight. Not Margot's type at all; she had to agree with Helen there.

She soon lost track of the various names as introductions were performed. Not all the women subjected her to the same, somewhat contemptuous scrutiny as Margot. For the most part they seemed friendly enough.

At dinner she found herself seated next to her host, while Logan was at the far end of the table on Margot's right-hand side. Aware with every fibre of the easy conversation going on between the two throughout the meal, she had difficulty in responding to the overtures of her near neighbours with anything beyond monosyllables. Duncan was the only one to persevere.

'You used to be in the Barston drama society, didn't you?' he said at one point. 'I direct the Priory Players based in Norwich. Would you be interested in joining? We need more younger people.'

'I might,' Caryn returned cautiously. 'Although it's a long time since I did any acting.'

Duncan laughed. 'Nothing in your life can be *such* a long time back! You have it all to come. I remember you from that very last production a couple of years or so back.'

Caryn laughed and wrinkled her nose, forgetting where she was for the moment. 'You don't have to be kind. I only got that part because someone was taken ill and I was the next nearest in age.'

He shook his head. 'Don't run yourself down. For a sixteen-year-old, you were very good.'

She'd been fifteen at the time, she could have told him, but who was counting?

'So I can put you down as a prospective member?' he insisted.

'Well . . . yes.' She wasn't at all certain about it, but it would have seemed churlish to say no. She added diffidently, 'Does Margot act too?'

The good humour faded a little from the pleasantly good-looking features. 'I'm afraid we don't share that particular interest.'

Nor so very many others, Caryn judged, reading between the lines. She wondered what Logan would think of her joining the society. Not that she needed to ask his permission, of course, but it would be nice to have his approval.

He was still talking animatedly with Margot—or, more correctly, she was doing most of the talking and he the listening, but the smile on his lips said it all. Even if he'd been telling the truth in denying any marital intentions in the past, he couldn't fail to compare the beautiful and sophisticated Mrs Ashley with his gauche new wife, she thought miserably.

The conversation she overheard through the open cloakroom window while washing her hands later did nothing to increase her confidence. The couple, whoever

they were, were out on the terrace with drinks and ciga-
rettes, their voices carrying on the still night air.

'So what do you think of her?' asked the woman.

The man laughed. 'She's certainly a lovely little thing!'

'Well, yes,' somewhat grudgingly. 'But with absolutely no dress sense, wouldn't you say?'

The laugh came again. '*I'd* say Logan's more interested
in what she's got underneath—although he paid a high
price for it.'

'There's a rumour going round that he had to be
married to inherit the estate, which might explain the
rush.'

'Rubbish! No court would uphold a condition like
that. Anyway, even if it were true, I can think of one
or two who'd have been only too glad to help him out,
without his having to resort to some teenager.'

'Ah, but could he have ruled the roost the same way?
Our little Caryn will be too grateful for her good fortune
to risk rocking the boat. She saw what was going on at
dinner between him and Margot, but you can bet she
won't call him out over it.'

Caryn stopped listening at that point. She would have
done better, she thought painfully, to have not listened
at all. Eavesdroppers rarely heard anything good about
themselves.

There was probably a lot of truth in what the woman
had said. If Logan had married anyone else just to
comply with his father's wishes, he might have found
himself far more restricted. With her he need make no
special effort; he knew only too well how to manage her.
Just toss her the occasional crumb when he felt like it,
and leave her hungering.

Only not any more, she told herself in sudden determination. From now on it was going to be a very different kettle of fish!

The party had split into small groups spread around the house, making it difficult to know which couple it had been out on the terrace. Not that it really mattered, Caryn reflected. The opinion was probably shared by all.

Logan was talking to Duncan, with Margot hovering impatiently. He appeared to be ignoring her, but that was just his way of staying in command. He looked devastating in the formal black and white, Caryn thought irrelevantly, and knew a moment of utter despair before her mettle rose again. Devastating he might be, *devastated* was what he was going to be!

One of the men, whose name she vaguely recalled was Tod something or other, moved purposefully across to where she stood just within the drawing-room door.

'Let me get you a drink,' he offered.

About to refuse, Caryn caught Logan's eye as he glanced her way, and summoned a bright smile instead. 'Thank you, I'll have a gin and tonic.'

He was back inside half a minute with the glass. He had also, she noted, found time to replenish his own. Whisky, her nose told her. That was all Logan ever drank—when he drank at all. It wasn't, he had told her once, by any means his favourite pastime. She didn't doubt it.

'You make me feel distinctly jaded,' said Tod with somewhat heavy-handed flattery. 'You make everybody here *look* distinctly jaded! Oh, to be eighteen again!'

'With no money and even less sense?' she quipped. 'Personally, I can't wait to be thirty.'

'You'll be a beauty whatever age.' He was looking directly into her eyes, the open admiration in his own balm to her injured spirit. 'Logan's a lucky man!'

Caryn lowered her gaze in demure deliberation. 'You're very kind.'

His laugh was appreciative. 'And you're not as guileless as you appear. Duncan tells me you're going to be joining the Priory. We're doing Quiet Weekend next. You'd be perfect as...'

'Hold on,' she protested. 'Even if I do join, I'd hardly expect to walk away with the lead first time.'

'I don't see why not, if you're up to it. It might cause some jealousy, but so what? The production's more important than a few bent egos.'

'Are there any other members here tonight?' she asked, not at all anxious to pursue that particular line. 'I know Margot isn't one.'

'Logan neither, of course.' His tone was bland. 'Seven of us, including Duncan himself. We're a close-knit set. We like doing things together. Let me freshen your drink.'

Disconcerted, Caryn looked down at the glass in her hand, hardly able to believe that she had almost drained the contents. She should say no, she knew; the effects were already making themselves felt. But so what? suggested her rebellious streak. One more wasn't going to make her drunk but it might keep her out of the doldrums. She was sick of trying to do the right thing.

The evening seemed to take on a whole new aspect after that, her tongue a new freedom. More than once she was aware of Logan watching her as she laughed and chatted, and flirted, and was delighted to show him just how well she could fit in when required. Let Margot have him. Why should she care? She was just beginning to realise what fun life could be.

How she got outside to the terrace she had no clear idea. She came to her senses when Tod started kissing her, his hand seeking her breast. There was no thrill in his caress, none of the tingling excitement she felt when Logan touched her; no pleasure at all in the kiss itself.

'What's wrong?' he demanded as she pushed him away. 'Don't you like being kissed?'

'No!' she said wildly. 'Not by you!'

'Then you shouldn't have come out here with me.' He sounded more amused than offended. 'You're just a kid, after all, aren't you, sweetheart? Not used to playing with the grown-ups.'

'If this kind of thing is part of it, then I'll stay the way I am,' she said with what dignity she could muster. 'I'm sorry if I gave you the wrong idea.'

His shrug made light of the affair. 'No problem. We'd better go back inside before your husband comes looking for you.'

Logan. The very thought of him catching the two of them a moment or so ago filled her with self-disgust. The drink wasn't wholly to blame. She had been trying to make him jealous. What he might have done if he had caught them, she hated to think.

'If you go back in looking like that, it's going to be thought I did a whole lot more than just kiss you,' remarked Tod drily. 'Smile, sweetheart. Pretend it never happened. I shan't report you to the headmaster.'

'Go to blazes!' she said furiously, and he grinned.

'That's better. Now you're talking my language.' He eyed her for a moment, then sighed. 'Look, we both made a mistake. No harm done.'

Not to him, perhaps, Caryn reflected wryly, but her self-esteem was at an even lower ebb than it had been a couple of hours ago.

It was inevitable, of course, that Logan should be facing the patio doors when they went back inside. She saw his eyes narrow as they went from her to that of the man at her back, and knew he had picked up the vibes. The hardening of his jawline was all the confirmation needed.

CHAPTER SEVEN

THE party started to break up around one o'clock. Logan waited until they were in the car and heading back to Whitegates before saying tautly, 'You stay away from Tod Garfield. Is that clear?'

The terse command, delivered without any kind of prologue, made Caryn's hackles rise. She wasn't a child to be spoken to that way; she wasn't going to be spoken to that way!

'That might be difficult,' she returned shortly. 'Duncan asked me to join the drama society. I believe Tod is a member.'

'You know damn well what I mean.' His tone was still clipped, his profile hard. 'His wife has enough of a problem trying to keep their marriage together, without you offering him encouragement.'

'I didn't offer him anything!' she denied.

'You let him take you outside.'

'For a breath of fresh air. It was getting stuffy in there.'

'You're not *that* naïve.'

'Apparently I am. Otherwise I'd have had more sense than to marry you in the first place!'

'You married me because you wanted to,' came the terse response. 'Because I could give you what you needed.'

Caryn drew in a shallow breath. 'I don't want your money!'

'I'm not talking about money. You have a highly developed libido. Marrying me was a way of gratifying it without kicking over the traces.'

'You mean I just wanted sex?' She was too hurt to be angry. 'If that was true, why would I have turned away from it on our wedding-night? Why would what Margot told me have bothered me at all?'

The laugh was brittle. 'You'd had your fantasies shattered. It was all right for me to be madly in love with you, even if you didn't have quite the same feelings for me. The off-on-off-again act was by way of retaliation. If I'd forced the issue, you'd have been delighted.'

'That's not true!'

'I think it is. Leaving you to stew for a few days was the worst kind of punishment. Last night you were desperate enough to rile me into taking you. Not,' Logan added with irony, 'that I was so loath. My own libido has been decidedly undernourished these last few days.' He paused, tone firming afresh. 'Anyway, I'd better be the only man you have physical contact with from now on. If I catch you so much as looking sideways at anyone else, you'll regret it. Understood?'

'Oh, perfectly.' The anger was coming through now, loud and clear. 'It's called dog-in-the-manger!'

'Not true. I want you all right. I'm just not prepared to turn a blind eye while you play the coquette with other men.'

'But I'm not supposed to complain when you do that kind of thing with other women, is that it?' she demanded. 'I'd have to be an idiot not to know what was going on between you and Margot tonight! Everyone knew!'

'Then everyone was wrong,' he came back flatly. 'And don't try to turn the tables on me that way. Contrary to general belief, attack isn't always the best means of defence.'

Caryn subsided into silence. He was never going to believe that she hadn't intentionally flirted with Tod. If the truth were only known, she wasn't so sure herself. The alcohol might have been partly to blame, but the desire to show Logan that he wasn't the only fish in the sea had been there to start with.

Whether or not he had any designs where Margot was concerned, there was no doubting the latter's interest. The woman had scarcely bothered to conceal it. She would, Caryn reflected, be keeping an eye open herself.

Apart from a light left burning in the hall, the house was in darkness when they reached it. Caryn went straight indoors while Logan garaged the car, and was already in the bathroom when he came upstairs.

He said nothing when she emerged, nor did he glance her way, but simply continued to undress. Caryn passed him by with averted gaze and got into bed, turning on her side facing away from him, the same way she had done every night since their marriage. If he attempted to touch her tonight after all he had said, she would spit in his eye! she vowed fiercely.

She tensed when he slid into the bed at last, heart missing a beat as he moved over to put a proprietorial arm about her waist. His hand moved up immediately to find her breast, fingers warm and supple and instantly arousing. It took every ounce of willpower she possessed not to respond.

'Don't try to shut me out,' he murmured against the nape of her neck. 'We're going to make the best of what we have.'

Caryn lay rigidly, every fibre alive to the feel of him at her back, chest so hard against her shoulder blades, knees tucking up under hers to bring her into even closer proximity. She wanted badly to give way to him, but there was a deep-down part of her that just wouldn't let go.

He moved his mouth down to her shoulder, pushing the narrow strap aside as he traversed the fine boning. His hand slid the length of her body to find the hem of her nightdress and begin a slow and tantalising pilgrimage along her calf, fingers seeking the ultra-sensitive spot at the back of her knee. Caryn held her breath in an effort to stop any sound from escaping her lips, trying to think of something else—*anything* but what Logan was doing to her.

He turned her on to her back to remove the nightdress altogether, dropping it to the floor at the side of the bed and bending his head to kiss the sharply indrawn flesh of her abdomen. Fists clenched so hard that her nails bit into her palms, Caryn tried to force herself to stay absolutely still as he moved inexorably downwards, but it was impossible when her whole body was clamouring to respond. Logan knew too much about female physiology—too much about everything!

The cry that rose in her throat at the first questing touch would not be denied exit. She clutched frantically at the dark head, unable to hold out any longer against the overwhelming sensation. It had been a losing battle from the start; Logan wasn't the kind to let an opposition he knew wasn't genuine put him off. S! *∶* would, Caryn knew in her heart, have been disappointed if he had simply accepted her professed reluctance.

Without thinking about it, she brought up a hand and found him as he came up and over her again, thrilling to the sense of vital power so barely contained. She heard his groan of pleasure, and knew a sudden flooding release. The movement came instinctively, gaining in dexterity as the last of her girlish inhibitions fell away; that same instinct brought him to her in swift, surging desire, locking him within long, silken limbs as they slid together in the wonderful, consummate merging.

It was the realisation of Logan's growing weight that brought Caryn slowly back to awareness. She shifted a little beneath him and felt him stir, as if just awakening from sleep. She hadn't wanted him to move away from her, and felt bereft when he rolled on to his side.

Turning to face him, she reached out a hand no longer tentative and drew the tip of a finger down through the hair on his chest, watching his face for his reaction. Expression enigmatic, he caught her by the wrist, bringing her hand up to his lips to kiss her fingers.

'Who showed you how to gratify a man that way?' he asked gruffly.

Caryn stiffened again, hardly able to believe what he was suggesting. 'No one ever showed me anything!' she denied with heat. 'You're the only one I ever...' She broke off, dragging her hand away and turning abruptly away from him. 'If that's what you think, you can get lost!' she flung at him, voice muffled by the pillow in which her face was buried.

There was a momentary pause, then he slid a hand over her shoulder, leaving it resting there when she resisted the gentle tug.

'I'm sorry,' he said softly. 'It was so unexpected. Last night you made no attempt to touch me at all; tonight you were every man's fantasy.'

'I thought it was what you wanted,' she said, voice still muffled by the pillow.

'It was—it is. You gave me the utmost pleasure. It's just that...'

'Just that you'd only expect it from someone more experienced,' she finished for him as he hesitated. 'Being so experienced with women yourself, of course!'

'It would be unusual, to say the least, if I'd reached the age I am without any experience at all,' came the dry reply. 'But that doesn't make me a hedonist.' This time the pull was more pronounced, turning her on to her back again and holding her there as he lifted himself on his other elbow to look into her face. 'Would it make any difference if I told you I'd never wanted any other woman more than I want you?'

It might, Caryn thought dully, if she believed it. He might want her as much as—especially now when she had proved herself capable of giving him the kind of response he was accustomed to receiving—but for how long?

'Well, *I* don't want *you*,' she said. 'Not any more.'

A faint smile touched the firm lips. 'Yes, you do. You like what I do to you too much to stand on principle. I could take you again right now.'

Caryn knew it was true. She even hoped he would. If she was given no choice in the matter then she had to submit—didn't she?

Logan stayed where he was, looking down at her with eyes that saw too much. This time the smile had a cynical edge to it. 'I think a little deprivation might do us both good,' he said, and pressed a swift kiss to her temple before subsiding on to his own side of the bed. 'Goodnight, Caryn.'

Lying there, body aching, she thought that she had never hated him more than she did at this moment. He was in charge all the way, and making sure she knew it.

*   *   *

The call came after dinner the following evening. Caryn took it in the drawing-room, only too conscious of Logan's presence, even though he was apparently engrossed in conversation with his mother.

'We have a casting meeting tomorrow evening,' said Duncan. 'Are you going to come?'

'Only if you promise not to throw me in at the deep end,' she responded, trying for a light note. 'As I told you last night, it's been some time since I did any acting.'

Duncan laughed. 'All the more reason to get started again, then. I'll pick you up.'

'I can drive into Norwich myself, thanks,' she said. 'What time?'

'Seven-thirty, Leyton Hall.'

'I know it.' Caryn found a moment to wonder what she did about dinner, but didn't like to bring the matter up. She was going to regret having said yes at all, she knew, but it was too late now to start changing her mind. She was only going to take a look, anyway. She didn't have to become a member if she didn't fancy it.

'So you're joining the Priory Players?' commented Helen when she returned to her seat. 'You were a leading light in Barston's little group a few years ago, weren't you?'

'I wouldn't exactly say that.' She added diffidently, 'The meeting is at seven-thirty. It makes it a bit awkward.'

'You mean because you'll miss dinner?' Helen shook her head. 'It isn't mandatory. You can have something earlier.' Her eyes went to her son. 'You're not thinking of going along too?'

'It isn't my scene,' he said.

'I understand they meet twice a week when they're rehearsing a production. It could be very tying.'

'I don't have anything else to do,' Caryn pointed out, forgetting for the moment that she hadn't even decided to join as yet.

Helen gave her a smile. 'I was thinking about if Logan wanted you to go somewhere with him on a rehearsal night, that's all.'

'That's a matter to be considered if and when,' said the latter without particular inflection. 'I don't see any great problem.'

Meaning he would naturally expect her to put his wishes first, Caryn surmised, meeting the steady grey eyes. Well, that remained to be seen. He might consider himself in charge, but she aimed to prove him wrong. She was her own person. The sooner he realised that, the better. There was a whole lot more to life than sexual fulfilment!

'Would you say there was anything in this rumour about the Ashleys, then?' Helen asked, abandoning the subject. 'You must have some idea after seeing the two of them together last night.'

Logan lifted his shoulders. '*You* saw the two of them together at the wedding. Your guess is as good as mine.'

'But I'm not as close as you are.'

'Used to be,' he corrected 'It's been two years, remember. Anyway, Duncan was never the confiding kind.'

Obviously not above enjoying a little gossip, his mother looked disappointed. 'Well, it's said there's no smoke without fire, so I imagine there has to be some truth in it. A child might have helped things along.'

Was that a hint for her? Caryn wondered. Did her mother-in-law sense the friction between her and Logan? She wasn't on the Pill, and Logan certainly hadn't bothered to use any form of protection, so it was even possible that she was already pregnant, she supposed.

The thought sent a sudden *frisson* down her spine. A baby: a tiny, helpless little being wholly reliant on her. She had never really contemplated it before.

'Caryn?' Logan was looking at her with lifted brows. 'I asked if you felt like coming with me on last rounds? Gordon is away for the night.'

She was too confused to dissemble, gazing back at him with eyes that reflected her inner turbulence. 'Sorry,' she got out. 'I was miles away. Yes, I'll come. I . . . feel like a walk.'

'If you're both going out, I'll go on up,' said Helen as they came to their feet. She was smiling but the lines about her eyes had deepened, the shadows beneath taken on a darker hue, emphasising the pallor of her skin. 'Be good.'

Logan made no attempt to start a conversation as the two of them made their way down to the stables. He seemed immersed in his thoughts. Concerned over his mother, Caryn surmised.

If the moon was up at all tonight, it was hidden behind the cloud. The breeze felt cool on her bare arms, making her wish she had put on a cover-up of some kind. It was warmer in the stable-yard though. Following in Logan's wake as he checked each animal, she felt a bit like a spare part. He didn't need her here. The horses were all he was thinking of now.

'Cold?' he asked, as they went through the archway to the second section.

'Not at the moment,' she acknowledged. 'I didn't expect it to have turned so chilly since teatime.'

'It happens,' he came back drily. 'This is England.'

'I imagine,' she said, 'that it's very different from this in Australia.'

'Yes, it is. It's winter out there now, but still warm enough.'

'Whereabouts is the farm?'

'Near Adelaide. We take horseback tours into the mountains as a sideline.'

'You must miss it.'

His shrug was non-commital. 'I got used to it.'

She said huskily, 'Was it really because of what happened that time that you went there in the first place?'

'That was a part of it, but I'd been considering the proposal for some time, so you don't need to feel wholly responsible.' The last with a faint smile. 'I was at university with Larry—my partner. He went out some years ago and got started, but he needed capital to expand. Blue River is a much bigger concern altogether than Whitegates. We count our area in square miles rather than acres.'

'Your mother told me you didn't get along too well with your father,' Caryn ventured.

'We didn't see eye-to-eye on everything, no. He regarded the stud as a hobby, and expected me to do the same. I needed a free hand.'

They had reached Oberon's stall. Caryn took an involuntary backward step as the great black head was thrust over the partition.

'It's all right. He's not with his mares now.' Logan spoke soothingly to the stallion, rubbing the velvety nose. 'Like all males, he responds to affection,' he added with irony. 'Let him scent you, then he'll know you next time.'

Caryn moved forward again cautiously, trying not to flinch as the animal snuffled at her. She even found the courage to reach up and pat the silky neck.

'About those riding lessons,' said Logan, watching her. 'I found a nice quiet mare that should be just the job.

You can progress to something a little more animated once you've mastered the rudiments. She's arriving tomorrow, but she'll need a little time to settle into strange surroundings, so we'll make a start in a couple of days. OK?'

'Fine.' Caryn would have accepted anything he suggested to retain this spirit of companionship. 'I'm looking forward to it.'

He laughed. 'You might change your mind when you feel what an hour in a saddle can do to you first time out!'

'I don't care,' she claimed recklessly. 'I'm going to be a horsewoman whatever it takes!'

'With that attitude, you can't fail.' Logan turned her away from the stall, lifting her chin to place a light but heartwarming kiss on her lips. 'Stick with it,' he said softly. 'We'll get there yet.'

He wasn't just referring to horse-riding, Caryn knew. Given time, she inferred, he could come to feel something deeper and more lasting than just physical desire. She hoped so. While it might be true that her feelings for him at sixteen had been more in the line of infatuation than love, what she felt for him now was so much more than that. Right at this moment she wanted badly to be in his arms—to prove to him that last night's performance had only been a start. There was nothing she wouldn't do to give him the kind of satisfaction the girl she had been hadn't known how to provide.

A sudden whinny from down towards the end of the row brought the dark head jerking upright again. Caryn went after him as he strode swiftly in the direction of the sound, but he had already disappeared into the roomy loose-box by the time she reached it.

For a moment, when she saw him kneeling in the straw with the horse looming over him, she thought he had been knocked down, then he got back to his feet and she saw the foal lying there still and silent.

'Is it dead?' she asked hesitantly.

'Not yet,' he said on a grim note. 'But not too far off. It looks like some kind of poisoning. I'll call the vet.'

There was a telephone in the tack room at the end of the row. Caryn hovered in the doorway while he made the call, wishing there were something she could do.

'There's nothing anyone can do until we find the cause of the problem,' Logan assured her when she said as much after he put the receiver down. 'I'm only making a rough guess.' He sounded unemotional. 'You'd better go on back to the house. I'll wait here for Andrew. He's only a few miles away. He should be here in ten minutes or so.'

'I'd like to stay,' she offered. 'Unless you'd prefer me to go?'

He shook his head. 'A rug would help keep her warm,' was all he said, but it was enough.

They spent the next ten minutes in the box, with Logan calming the fraught mother while Caryn knelt in the straw by the side of the small, sick animal—the same one she had petted only the day before. It seemed to ease the foal's breathing when its head was raised a little. Caryn supported it in her lap, oblivious of the spreading saliva stain on her skirt front. Apart from the Gregory family cat, who wasn't of a particularly affectionate nature, she had never held an animal this close before. For the first time she could begin to understand the depth of feeling they aroused in people.

She was quick to get out of the way once the vet arrived, although she went no farther than the door, watching anxiously as he examined the foal. The shake of his head when he sat back on his heels was like a shaft through the heart.

'Too far gone for any recovery, I'm afraid,' he said. The kindest thing I can do is put her down. A post-mortem is the only way I'm going to be able to tell what caused it.'

Logan nodded, apparently unmoved. 'I'll put Lucy in the spare box.'

Caryn swung the lower half of the stable door open for him as he led the reluctant mare forth, unable to stop the tears welling in her eyes.

'I'm so sorry,' she said softly.

The lean features remained expressionless. 'One of those things you'll have to learn to accept. Go on back to the house now. I'll be up in a little while.'

This time she made no demur about it. There was no point in staying any longer. The vet would do what he had to do, and that would be that. One foal gone, others still alive and kicking, and little room for sentiment. Logan might have learned to take such happenings in his stride, but she doubted if she ever could.

She was in bed when he did return to the house. She wanted to say something, but she couldn't think *what* to say. When he finally got into bed she waited for his arm to come about her, but she waited in vain. Only bare moments later, or so it seemed, his breathing deepened into sleep. It was a long time before she managed to follow suit.

Mrs Lawson provided a by no means makeshift meal for one at six o'clock, leaving Caryn feeling guilty for disrupting the housekeeper's routine, although the woman didn't appear to be in the least bit put out. Logan still hadn't put in an appearance by the time she left for Norwich. According to Helen, he'd gone to Thetford around four-thirty to chase up some supplier.

As usual, Caryn had still been asleep when he got up that morning, but he had seemed relaxed enough at lunchtime. He hadn't said anything to her about going to Thetford, but then why should he? She was only his wife, not his keeper.

The drive into Norwich was easy enough, the evening traffic light. She parked the car round the back of the hall at twenty-five minutes past seven, and made her way inside to find most of the membership already there before her.

'Glad you could make it,' said Duncan. 'I thought you might change your mind. You already know one or two people, of course, but come and meet the rest.'

As on the Monday evening, Caryn found herself unable to remember all the names thrown at her over the next few minutes. While she was certainly the youngest person there, there were others not all that much older, she was glad to note. Several people she had already met at the Ashleys', of course. Tod in particular greeted her like an old friend.

His wife, Avril, looked on with a resigned expression as he exerted his not inconsiderable charm. He was, Caryn was bound to acknowledge, extremely attractive with his carefully casual mane of blond hair and wicked eyes, but he still made little impact on her.

To her relief, he made no attempt to put her name forward when they got down to casting. The main roles had already been decided, anyway, she realised, as Duncan read out names from a list.

She was gratified to be asked to take the prompt for this coming production, although a little reticent too, until it dawned on her that no one else really wanted the job.

At ten o'clock, coffee and biscuits were served as a conclusion to what Duncan termed a very satisfactory evening. It was while drinking the coffee and chatting sociably with Tod and Avril and one or two other members that Caryn felt the bottom drop out of her world. Duncan was talking with another group only a few feet away, but his voice carried clearly:

'Haven't seen her since lunchtime. She went to Thetford to visit her cousin.'

He was referring to Margot, of course, Caryn thought numbly. It was hardly a coincidence that Logan should have gone to the same place.

Whatever Margot might have in mind, Logan was hardly going to risk ruining his mother's remaining few months of life by having her guess how far from a love match his marriage really was, but that didn't mean he wouldn't be prepared to indulge in an affair with a beautiful and mature former lover who could meet him on his own level. Having the best of both worlds, it was called.

'You're looking very pensive all of a sudden,' commented Tod, watching her curiously. 'Something wrong?'

Caryn summoned a smile and shook her head. 'Just a passing thought.'

'You should try and persuade Logan to join us,' said Avril. 'He has an excellent voice, and a very good presence.'

'But different interests,' rejoined her husband before Caryn could answer.

And he had a very good idea what they were, she guessed, meeting his eyes. How like men were men?

It was a quarter to eleven before the last few stragglers finally left. Caryn had lingered deliberately, and would have continued to do so had anyone else shown any inclination.

'Lock all your doors,' warned Duncan as she got into the Rover. 'And don't stop for anything.'

'I won't,' she assured him, wondering if he would feel it necessary to caution any lone female driver that way. She wasn't all that used to night driving, she was bound to admit; her father hadn't liked her taking the car after dark. All the same, he didn't need to worry about her. She waved a cheery hand. 'See you all on Friday.'

Accustomed though she was to the route by daylight, she still managed to miss the Somerton turn-off, and found herself crossing Filby Broad before she realised. She briefly contemplated carrying on and taking the coast road, but it was a long way round. There had been a sign for Rollesby a little way back, she recalled. She could cut across country to Martham from there and save herself a few miles.

Finding the road again was no great problem, but she had forgotten how comparatively minor it was. Unlit too, of course, although the Rover's headlights cut a wide swathe ahead. It was going to be midnight before she reached Whitegates, she realised, catching a glimpse of the dashboard clock. Logan would wonder what on earth had happened.

So let him wonder, she thought with acrimony. He could while away the time thinking about the afternoon and evening he had spent with Margot!

It hurt to think about it herself. They would have made love for certain. Men like Logan and women like Margot were hardly the kind of people to settle for a chaste kiss or two.

While she would find it difficult to accuse him openly, there was no way she could turn a blind eye and pretend that nothing had happened either. At present she couldn't decide *how* she was going to handle the situation.

CHAPTER EIGHT

THE dashboard clock was reading five minutes past twelve when she finally reached Whitegates. Logan had left the Mercedes out on the drive, making her wonder just what time *he* had got home. Reluctant to face him, Caryn took the time and trouble to garage the Rover, then used the side door to gain access to the house via the connecting covered passage.

Logan was standing in the study doorway when she got inside. His expression left her in little doubt of his mood.

'Where the devil have you been?' he clipped. 'Duncan said you left well before eleven!'

'I missed the turning,' she replied with an airiness she was far from feeling. 'I cut across country.'

'At this time of night!'

'I knew the way,' she defended. 'It just took a bit longer than I anticipated.'

'And supposing you'd had an accident, or the car had broken down? You could have been out there all night, for God's sake!'

Caryn drew in a steadying breath, determined not to show any emotion. 'But I didn't have an accident and the car didn't break down, so it's all right, isn't it?'

Logan drew in an audible breath of his own, face set. 'No, it damn well isn't all right! And if you don't have the sense to see it, then you can leave the car in the garage in future!'

Blue eyes flashed as anger rose in her. 'I'll do that if and when your mother tells me I can't use it, considering that it's still her car. I'm not sixteen any more, Logan— or hadn't you noticed?'

'In some respects, there's little difference,' he returned grimly. 'Had it occurred to you that I might be worried about you?'

'No, it hadn't. I don't expect to have to account for my movements.' She added with deliberation, 'After all, I don't ask you to account for yours.'

Some flicker of unreadable expression came and went in the grey eyes. '*I'm* not in the habit of putting myself at risk.'

He was avoiding the implied question, Caryn thought, and took that as proof positive of his guilt.

'Nor am I,' she responded bitingly. 'I never had an accident yet, and a car as new as the Rover is hardly likely to break down.' She made a pretence of smothering a yawn with the back of her hand. 'Anyway, I'm going to bed.'

He made no move to intercept her as she crossed the hall to the stairs. He made no move at all, just continued to stand there in the doorway. She could feel his eyes on her as she mounted the treads, but she refused to look back. Let him think what he liked. She owed him no apologies.

Only on reaching the bedroom did she start to consider the night still to come. If he attempted to touch her she would throw the whole thing in his face, she vowed fiercely. This marriage had been doomed to failure from the start. Logan only wanted her at all because she was there and available and he had to have some kind of recompense for his sacrifice. But she was through being made a fool of!

He was only just taking off his shirt when she emerged from the bathroom, so he must have been quite a while following her upstairs. Caryn made to pass him, only to be brought up short by the hand that clamped about her wrist, yanking her round to face him.

'What happened tonight?' he demanded. 'Has Tod been up to his tricks again?'

The effrontery of it, knowing what she knew, took her breath away. The accusation trembled on her lips, but was overtaken by a sudden pressing urge to hit him in the only place it might reckon.

'What tricks are we talking about?' she asked, widening her eyes in mock innocence at him.

Grey eyes narrowed. 'Don't play that kind of game with me. You've made it obvious that you're attracted to him.'

'So what if I am?' she retorted recklessly. 'He's an attractive man, who treats me like a woman, not some kid incapable of looking after herself!'

'He reacts to you the same way he reacts to any pretty face other than his wife's, so don't run away with the idea that you're something special in his life.' Logan's tone was scathing. 'As to treating you like a woman, I might feel more inclined to do that myself if you tried acting like one more often!'

'So sorry if I fail to match up to what you're used to,' she flung at him, pierced through by the intimation. 'I haven't had the same practice!'

'I'm not talking about sex,' he said. 'The way you acted when you came in just now is what I'm on about. I should have put you across my knee!'

Caryn eyed him with loathing. 'That just about sums up your whole attitude!'

'It sums up the real problem,' he countered. 'You haven't grown up yet. Living your whole life in a town like Barston hasn't helped. You should have broadened your horizons—seen something of the world.'

'And who else would you have found to do what I did? Who else would have been stupid enough!'

'If you hadn't been around I might not have bothered to fulfil the condition at all,' he said. 'It isn't as if I'm going to spend the rest of my life here.'

Caryn stared at him, the wind taken completely out of her sails. 'Are you telling me it's your intention to go back to Australia after your mother is . . . gone?' she got out.

Logan hesitated, mouth wryly slanted. 'Is that so surprising? It's a different world out there. It makes England feel claustrophobic.'

'And what about me?' she asked, and saw the slant increase.

'It's customary for a wife to be with her husband.'

'I might not want to be.'

'That's a decision you'll have to make if and when the time comes.' His tone had steadied. 'I couldn't force you—any more than I could *force* you to do anything.'

Caryn said stiffly, 'Does your mother know?'

'No. And I'd prefer that she remain in ignorance, so if you're thinking of telling her, don't.'

'I wouldn't dream of destroying her illusions.' She directed a pointed glance at the hand still holding her by the wrist. 'Do you mind letting go of me, please? I'd like to go to bed.'

For a brief but dangerous moment his grasp actually tightened, his eyes like twin barbs, then he shrugged and released her.

'By all means go to bed.'

She did so, lying there in heart-heavy silence and rigid stillness while he finished undressing. Only when the shower began running did she stir cramped muscles, rolling on to her back to gaze unseeingly at the ceiling. He had never intended to stay here at Whitegates; she was sure of it now. Everything he had done had been purely for his mother's sake. Oh, yes, he would take her with him if she wanted to go, but it wasn't essential. If she refused it would solve the whole problem.

Australia. Had their marriage been a normal one she would have been prepared to follow him anywhere in the world, but things would be no different out there. Worse, in fact, because while he might still find some novelty value in making love to her now, he would probably be bored out of his mind with her by then.

The shower was turned off and silence returned, broken only by the sound of the wind in the trees outside. When the bathroom door opened, Caryn turned on to her side again, as close to the edge of the mattress as she could get without actually falling out of the bed altogether. She couldn't bear him near her, she thought numbly. If he touched her at all, she would scream!

He made no attempt. Several minutes passed before he spoke, voice quiet but no less forceful for it.

'We're going to have to reach some kind of understanding. It can't go on like this. If you want to stay with the society, fine, but you keep Tod Garfield at arm's length in future.'

Once again there was her cue to counter-accuse, yet she somehow couldn't bring herself to say the words. Perhaps, a small voice at the back of her mind suggested, because she didn't really want confirmation.

'His arm's length, or mine?' she asked with deliberation.

'I'm not joking,' Logan growled. 'Just take note.'

Otherwise what? it was on the tip of her tongue to retort, but she bit it back. Defiance of that nature *was* less than adult—and asking for retaliation. That he was capable of resorting to the tactics he had threatened earlier if goaded far enough, she didn't doubt for a moment. He was capable of anything.

'You're learning,' he said sardonically when she remained silent. 'There may be hope yet.'

Not for the kind of relationship she had once visualised, Caryn reflected achingly. That was right out of the window!

Helen's suggestion the following morning that they go for a run in the car and have lunch out somewhere gave her cause for hesitation, much as she liked the idea.

'Are you sure you feel up to it?' she asked diffidently, registering her mother-in-law's lack of colour and general air of lassitude.

'Driving, no; being driven, yes,' came the answer. 'Just up the coast a way. Anything,' she added with sudden urgency, 'to be out and about. I can't spend the rest of my life cooped up here waiting for it to happen. I need to live a little!'

Caryn could understand that. What she was unsure about was the wisdom of putting extra strain on a system already overloaded. Yet did it really matter in the end? she asked herself. If faced with the same choice, wouldn't she also prefer to enjoy the here and now?

They took the coast road up through Waxham and Happisburgh as far as Mundesley, pausing to take a look at the famous smock windmill complete with cap and sails, then turning inland to seek out a country pub near the village of Trunch, that Caryn had heard provided particularly good food.

They, and a party of four obvious holiday makers, were the only lunchtime customers, but the food was certainly good, to say nothing of plentiful. Caryn's choice of a seafood platter would have been more than sufficient for two people.

Helen had mushroom omelette. She was showing more appetite than usual, Caryn reflected, watching her eat. They had had the windows down to make the most of the fresh air, and it seemed to have done her some good.

'We must do this more often,' she said impulsively.

'It would be nice,' Helen agreed. 'But I'm not going to let you give me all your time, Caryn. Logan said at dinner last night that the pony he bought for you has settled in well enough for you to start those riding lessons. 'You *do* want to learn to ride, don't you?'

'Yes.' Caryn hesitated, wondering how to put the question. 'Logan was home for dinner, then?' she said on as casual a note as she could manage. 'I thought he'd stayed out.'

'He came in not long after you left.' Helen smiled as if at a passing thought. 'He was worried about you driving home on your own in the dark, although I assured him you'd be all right. The Bannister males were always protective of their womenfolk.'

Possessive might be a better word, thought Caryn drily. So Logan hadn't been out all evening too, but that still left several hours unaccounted for. If she hadn't overheard Duncan saying where Margot had gone, she would have thought little of it. She almost wished she hadn't overheard. Sometimes ignorance was better than knowledge.

His fears last night hadn't only been in the interests of her safety. He had also been concerned about what she might be getting up to with Tod. He might need other women, but *she* must take no interest in other men!

'You're looking very pensive,' commented Helen, jerking her out of her thoughts. 'Everything *is* all right with the two of you, isn't it?'

Caryn forced a smile. 'Everything is fine. I'd just drifted off, that's all.'

'You would tell me if there were anything worrying you?' her mother-in-law insisted, not wholly deceived. 'I know Logan can be a little domineering at times— just as his father was—and that you have a very definite mind of your own, but there's such a thing as compromise.'

'With most of it coming from my side,' Caryn couldn't help retorting, and saw understanding in the other eyes.

'A clever woman can have things her own way and still leave a man's pride intact,' she said softly. 'It's all a matter of how much she cares for him.'

'Women have pride too,' Caryn pointed out, trying not to sound too serious about it.

'Not the same thing, dear. We're capable of rising above it.' Helen paused, resting a thoughtful regard on the younger face opposite. 'The fifteen years between you won't make it any easier, but they're not insurmountable.'

'No, of course they're not.' Caryn could make no other reply. 'It's all right, Helen. Really. I'm just not used to being married yet.'

'Well, it has only been a week.'

One week, Caryn thought hollowly, and already the cracks were showing. Margot aside, she might have been prepared to follow Helen's advice and learn to handle Logan more subtly, but it was asking too much to ignore what she knew.

It was mid-afternoon when they got back to Whitegates. Finding Logan there waiting for them was a surprise to them both.

'You're supposed to be resting,' he said brusquely to his mother, taking stock of the shadows under her eyes. 'Not gallivanting around the countryside!'

'I've all the time in the world to rest,' she answered. 'In any case, it doesn't take any effort to sit in a car while someone else does the chauffering. Caryn is an excellent driver. I've every confidence in her.'

Judging from the expression that crossed the lean features as he glanced her way, the confidence wasn't shared, Caryn gathered. She returned his gaze stonily for a moment before looking back to his mother with a smile. 'I'm ready and willing any time you feel like an outing. You only have to say.'

Helen smiled back. 'Thank you, dear. It's so nice to have another woman for company. Mrs Lawson is a very good housekeeper, but she isn't the world's greatest conversationalist.' She glanced at her watch. 'I think I'll go and have a nap until tea.'

The two left below watched her slowly mount the stairs. She looked fatigued, Caryn was bound to acknowledge; but then she often looked the same just sitting around the house.

'The next time I'll want to know where you're going,' said Logan unequivocally.

Caryn kept her tone level. 'Supposing you're not around to tell?'

'Then leave a message. The direction you're thinking of taking would be a help in itself if anything should happen.'

'Such as my crashing the car, you mean?'

'It's always a possibility, even for the best of drivers,' he returned with irony. 'Just as it's possible for any car to develop some mechanical fault. Supposing you were stuck out on some country lane somewhere and couldn't get to a phone?'

'You could always have a car phone put in,' she suggested. 'Like the one in the Mercedes. That way there wouldn't be any problem.'

'It would reduce the odds, certainly,' he conceded. 'All right, I'll see to it. But I'll still want to know your plans.'

Where his mother was concerned, she could make no objection, Caryn acknowledged. He had a right to be kept in the picture. 'I'll make sure of it,' she said.

'Good.' He studied her for a moment with an odd expression in his eyes, as if weighing something in balance, then gave a brief dismissive shrug. 'I came back to ask if you were ready for the first lesson? There's still time before tea.'

She wasn't ready, but could find no excuse to refuse. 'What do I wear?' she asked resignedly.

'Jeans and walking shoes will do until we get you fixed up with the proper gear. I'll find you a spare hat for the present, but you'll need to be measured for one before you do any serious riding. You'll be on the lunging rein today.'

So what was new? Caryn reflected with a cynicism that was coming far too easily these days.

He waited downstairs for her while she went up to change. Learning to ride had been part of her aim towards forging a closer relationship, but she doubted now if it would make any difference. The gap had widened too far already.

So close it again, said a sudden new voice at the back of her mind. *Make* this marriage work. If it's worth having at all, then it's worth fighting for.

Yes, but how? she asked the reflection in the mirror as she fastened the buttons of her shirt. Margot had all the advantages of age and experience. All she had was youth and uncertainty. Logan had married her for all the wrong reasons; it was going to take more than just the wish to make him feel the way she wanted him to feel about her.

Despite her initial reluctance, she found the friendly little bay mare named Dorea irresistible. Logan showed her first how to tack up, saying she would be doing it for herself from now on. Caryn was a little wary when it came to sliding the bit between the formidable-looking teeth, but Dorea accepted it without protest, giving her a little more confidence in reaching under the rounded belly for the girths, and a real sense of accomplishment when the last strap was fastened.

'Wait a couple of seconds, then pull it in another notch,' Logan instructed. 'They blow themselves out deliberately to gain room, but if the girths are slack the saddle will slip. It won't hurt her.'

Caryn wasn't so sure, but she did as she was told, gaining a reproachful backward look from the mare. Hoisted into the saddle by Logan's hand under her bent leg, she seemed a long way from the ground. The only other times she had sat on a horse it had been even further, of course, but then she'd had Logan at her back, holding her steady. She wished he were there now, not so much for safety as for the sheer contact.

He led the pair of them into the smaller of the two fenced exercise rings, and spent ten minutes walking them round in a circle governed by the long lunging rein he held. Caryn began to enjoy the movement, to relax into it. The mingled smell of leather and warm horseflesh was aphrodisiacal.

'You seem to have a natural seat,' Logan commented. 'Are you ready to try the trot?'

She was, Caryn thought elatedly, ready for anything! 'Why not?' she agreed.

Moments later she was ready to quit altogether. The co-ordination required to lift out of the saddle in time with the mare's movements seemed beyond her, resulting in a jolting, teeth-jarring progress that threatened to unseat her.

'I can't do it!' she gasped for the umpteenth time. 'Stop it, Logan!'

'Yes, you can,' he insisted. 'Press your weight into the stirrups and lift. Find the rhythm.'

And suddenly it was there, as natural as breathing, once mastered. Slow or fast, she could handle it. Laughing, eyes sparkling, she was even ready to protest when Logan called a halt.

'That's enough for today,' he said firmly, coming to hold the mare's head. 'Not like that,' he added as she began to dismount. 'Kick both feet free of the stirrups and bring your right leg over her back, then slide down to the ground. That way you don't risk getting dragged.'

She did so, moving up to pat the silky neck with a whole new sense of rapport. 'We'll be cantering tomorrow, Dorea!'

'That's the spirit,' Logan applauded. He both looked and sounded light-hearted himself. 'You'll be ready to ride out by the weekend. Under supervision, of course.'

'I'll look forward to it,' she said, and meant it.

He lifted a quizzical brow. 'You don't object to being supervised?'

'There's supervision and supervision,' she conceded. 'I'm hardly qualified to go off riding on my own.'

'But you do consider yourself well qualified to wander around country lanes at night on your own?'

'That's different. I had the car doors locked.'

'Little deterrent to a determined attacker. There may have been a time when you'd have been safe enough, but these days you can't afford to take any chances.' His tone was still easy. 'Duncan has offered to pick you up for rehearsals and bring you home again afterwards. I'd be happier that way.'

Certain, too, that she wasn't up to any mischief with Tod, came the thought. Eyes on the mare, she said jerkily, 'You'd no right to make arrangements with Duncan behind my back.'

'I didn't say I'd accepted the offer, just that I'd prefer you did.' There was a hint of impatience in his voice now. 'When are you going to stop playing the rebellious teenager and start using a little common sense?'

'About the same time you stop playing the solicitous husband and start being honest with yourself!' she flashed, abandoning restraint in the searing anger of the moment. 'You don't trust me, do you? You think I'm capable of encouraging Tod! Well, what's sauce for the gander is sauce for the goose!'

Disturbed by the sudden high-tension atmosphere, the mare moved restlessly. Logan held her in check, calming her with a soothing word before turning a steely-eyed gaze back to Caryn, who had stepped aside to avoid the iron-shod hooves.

'We'll continue this after Dorea is back in her stall,' he said quietly. 'Take her head and speak to her. Let her know it's not her you're angry with.'

Caryn did as he said, already regretting the outburst.
She had more or less accused him, and he wasn't going
to let it pass. He would deny any involvement with
Margot, of course. She had no proof, only circum-
stantial evidence.

He made her lead the mare back to her stall, take off
her tack and rub her down before leaving her. Had it
not been for what she knew was to come, Caryn would
have enjoyed the whole process. On the surface Logan
appeared undisturbed, but there was a certain line to his
jaw that intimated a far different mood within.

'That will do for now,' he said at length. 'We'll take
a walk.'

They did so in silence for the first few minutes. Caryn
couldn't think of anything to say, and Logan made no
attempt to speak. He wasn't touching her in any way,
yet she was, as always, sensitised to his very presence,
skin tingling, stomach muscles fluttering, pulses
quickened.

Once clear of the yards, he took the track that led
down to the river, stopping at the first gate to lean his
elbows and look out over the fields beyond.

'All right,' he said levelly. 'Let's have it.'

Throat tight and dry, Caryn searched her mind for
some get-out. In some ways a denial would be as bad
as an admittance, because she still wouldn't know for
sure.

'I resent you asking Duncan to keep an eye on me,'
she prevaricated. 'Perhaps it was a bit foolish to cut
across country last night, but the likelihood of anything
happening was very slim.'

'We'll go into that later,' he said. 'Right now I want
to know what the goose and gander comment was supposed to be about.'

There was no getting off the hook, she acknowledged fatalistically. So spill it out.

'I'd have thought it spoke for itself. Why should I steer clear of Tod, when you're seeing Margot on the side?'

If she really had anticipated an immediate denial, she was to be disappointed. Logan didn't bat an eyelid, simply turned his head and studied her thoughtfully. 'What gave you that idea?'

'You went to Thetford yesterday afternoon,' she said. 'I happen to know that Margot was there too.'

'That's right,' he agreed. 'She was.'

The calm affirmation sent her heart plummeting. She gazed at him with darkened eyes, struggling to keep her emotions under control. 'I suppose you'll be telling me next that it was pure coincidence!'

'No, it was an arranged meeting.' His lips twisted as her face went rigid. 'But not for the purpose you're suggesting.'

'Then what?'

'I'm afraid that's between the two of us.' He shook his head as she opened her mouth to protest. 'You'll just have to trust me, Caryn.'

'The same way you trust me?' she demanded.

His sigh came deep. 'I know Tod Garfield of old. We were rivals more than once. He'd like nothing better than to put a wedge between us—especially considering the state of his own marriage.'

'He and Avril seem to get along all right,' she said, momentarily sidetracked.

'Only because she puts a good face on it in public. If she didn't know him for what he is when they got married, she certainly does now.'

'You mean *she* confided in you as well?' Caryn made no effort to keep the sarcasm from her voice.

'She doesn't need to confide in me. I've known her a long time too.'

'Then perhaps you should have married her yourself and saved her from him!'

'It was never that kind of relationship.' Logan straightened his position abruptly. 'We're not getting anywhere like this. If you won't accept Duncan's offer, I'll drive you in to rehearsals myself. At least then I'd be sure of getting you home again safely.'

'And hang around for three hours until we've finished? Or did you have some other pastime in mind?'

The look he gave her was calculated. 'You really do go all out for reprisals. If it will set your mind at rest, I'll even join the damned society!'

'I wouldn't want you making any sacrifices for me!' Caryn retorted.

'It's either that, or you go with Duncan as arranged,' he came back hardily. 'I mean it, Caryn. I'm sure my mother will see the sense in it too.'

'In other words, *you'll* see that she withdraws use of the Rover! Well, fine. Go ahead! Caryn was too embittered to care what she was saying; all she wanted was to penetrate that hide of his. 'Just don't expect me to believe that you and Margot only talked together. How naïve do you think I am?'

Just for a moment he looked as if she might have succeeded in undermining his control. His teeth came together in an audible snap and his eyes blazed. But only for a moment, then he was in command of himself again, the anger held in check.

'Believe what you want to believe,' he said. 'I have work to do.'

Caryn stood rooted as he headed back up the track, only now beginning to consider that she just might be wrong. She wanted to call him back, but his name stuck in her throat. It was unlikely that he would respond, anyway. He had looked too much like a man who had reached the end of his tether.

On the other hand, why else would he have arranged to meet Margot in secret if it weren't for the obvious reason? she asked herself in mitigation. They'd been lovers in the past, and Margot had made it more than plain on Monday evening that she was still interested in him. For a man like Logan, one woman—especially an inadequate one—just wasn't enough. He'd been accustomed to freedom of choice all his adult years. A little thing like marriage wasn't going to tie him down.

One week, and it had come to this, she thought wretchedly, watching the tall figure moving ever further away from her. Where did they go from here?

CHAPTER NINE

HELEN was waiting with tea on the terrace when Caryn got back to the house.

'I was beginning to think I'd been deserted,' said the former lightly. 'Been for a walk, have you?'

'No, a riding lesson.' Caryn took a seat and accepted the cup poured for her. 'Thanks.'

'And how did it go?' asked her mother-in-law.

'Fine.' It was an effort to keep her voice from reflecting her inner despondency. 'Very enjoyable.'

'Then you'll be keeping it up?'

There was only one answer Caryn could make. 'Of course.'

'That's good. All marriages benefit from shared interests. You should perhaps persuade Logan to join the drama society too.'

'As a matter of fact, he already offered.' This time there was no disguising her feelings. 'But only to stop me from driving home alone, which isn't exactly an ideal reason.'

Helen winged a shrewd glance. 'It's an understandable one in this day and age. There was a young woman attacked in town only the other night just walking to her car. Logan is naturally concerned that the same thing doesn't happen to you.'

'Hardly likely unless I lingered until everyone else had gone. Anyway, I doubt if he'd be as concerned if I were ten years older.'

'You'd rather he were indifferent to what might happen to you?' Helen's tone had sharpened just a fraction.

'Your age might make him more protective, I dare say, but that's surely no crime?'

Caryn bit her lip, aware of having annoyed the older woman. 'No, of course it isn't,' she said. 'It's just that it makes me feel like a schoolgirl still.'

'And you'd prefer to be seen as a responsible married woman?' Helen was smiling again, albeit with a certain reservation. 'Don't be in too much of a hurry to relinquish your youth. It only comes the once. In the meantime, would it really be such a hardship to indulge Logan? After all, if he's even prepared to join the society himself...'

Faced with that, Caryn gave in. 'He doesn't have to. Duncan said he would pick me up.'

'Well, then, it's your choice.'

A very limited choice, Caryn reflected, but this time kept her own counsel. Helen might talk about compromise, but where her son was concerned the word didn't exist.

Reluctant to face Logan again as yet, she showered and dressed for the evening before he returned to the house, and spent the next hour or so in the library with a book.

Having time to read, with so much literature readily available, was a pleasure on which she was only just beginning to capitalise. Many would consider themselves fortunate to have what she had, she knew, but she also knew that she would willingly give up everything else just to hear Logan say 'I love you', and mean it from the heart.

He was first down. Caryn got to her feet to go and replace the book she had been reading to its place, pretending to peruse other titles as he went to pour himself a drink.

Above petty gestures, he poured a sherry for her too, and another in readiness for his mother's arrival, then took a seat on the same sofa Caryn had been occupying. It would be a petty gesture on her part, she acknowledged wryly, if she deliberately chose another seat herself because of this afternoon's contretemps.

The sofa was only made for two. Without consciously sitting on the far side of her own cushion, she found it impossible to remain altogether detached from contact. The long-sleeved cream shirt he had on was almost a perfect match in colour with her blouse. Like a pair of book-ends, she found herself thinking with a hint of humour.

Acting on impulse, she said softly, 'I've decided to let Duncan take me to rehearsals after all.'

'Why the sudden change of mind?' Logan asked.

'Something your mother said. I——'

'Good to know you take notice of someone!' came the clipped response before she could go any further. 'We'll talk about it later.'

'There's nothing to talk about.' Caryn was past being co-operative. 'You got your own way. Isn't that enough?'

'Is that all...?' He broke off abruptly, mouth compressing, then took a long swallow from his whisky glass, putting it down again to add with restraint, 'I said later.'

Helen's arrival was a welcome relief, although it was obvious that she was aware of the atmosphere between the two of them from the way her glance went from one to the other. She made no comment, but she looked troubled. Caryn would have given a great deal to reassure her, only what reassurance was there? Logan wanted total capitulation to his authority, and that far she just wasn't prepared to go.

The evening went through its phases. Logan showed no outward sign of disharmony in his treatment of her, but she knew it was there. Things couldn't go on like this, she thought unhappily. They didn't have a marriage, they had a travesty!

The conversation centred mainly on Logan's plans for the stud, though chiefly, Caryn was bound to admit, at Helen's prompting. She found the subject interesting enough herself now that she was beginning to acquire some feeling for the animals. She had just never realised how exhilarating it was to be in control of such power, to feel silken muscles moving to her command. Right now the stallions intimidated her with their size and strength and temperament, but she might even learn to handle them too given time and opportunity. All it took was the will.

'You've certainly got things moving quickly,' Helen observed on learning that work was due to start on the stable extensions and indoor arena the following week. 'You'll have the whole thing up and running by the end of the summer, which means you can start looking round for a buyer.' She gave a faint smile as her son's head jerked up. 'You don't really think I expected you to stay on for good, did you? I've seen the way you live over there, remember. I know how constricting you must find it here now. I'm selfish enough to want you with me for what time I have left, but no more than that.'

'You always did see through me,' Logan returned on a wry note. 'If I do go back, I'll make sure it goes to the right kind of people.'

'Why the *if*? You know it's what you want.' Her eyes moved to Caryn. 'How do you feel about it?'

'I haven't had chance to think about it,' she prevaricated. She moved her head in a gesture of distress. 'I don't know how you can talk about it all so calmly!'

'I've had the last eighteen months or so to accustom myself,' came the reply. 'There's no cure for what I've got, only remission, and time's running out on that.' Her smile came again. 'I'm not afraid of dying, dear. I've had a good life. The secret is to make the most of it all, because you never know what's around the corner. It's a lot to ask, I know, but I'd be utterly content if you and Logan managed to produce a grandchild for me before I went.'

'We'll do our best,' Caryn promised recklessly, not giving herself time to consider what she was saying. 'Won't we, Logan?'

'By all means.' His tone was level, his expression unrevealing.

'In which case, I'll go to bed and dream about it,' said his mother.

Silence reigned for several minutes after she had left the room. Logan was the first to break it.

'Is that what you really want?' he asked. 'Or were you just saying it to please her?'

It was a difficult question, made even more so by her inability to read his mind. 'I don't have any objections if you don't,' she said at length.

'That wasn't the question. Do you *want* a baby at eighteen?'

'I'd be nineteen by the time I had one, even if it happened right away.' She wasn't looking at him directly. 'It might even have happened already.'

'Yes, I know. A lack of forethought on my part. I should have considered.'

Except that he had been too angry initially that first night to think about such things, Caryn reflected. She had goaded him too far.

'If it has, then there's no decision to make,' she said on a practical note. 'But in any case, having promised your mother...'

'She was indulging in emotional blackmail. You don't have to feel obligated by any promises.'

'You might find it easy to break your word,' she retorted shortly, 'but I don't! A promise is a promise.'

'Fine.' His tone was equally short. 'Then we'd better get down to it, hadn't we.'

Caryn gazed up at him without moving as he got to his feet, heart beating fast and hard. She wanted his lovemaking desperately, but there was so much still missing. A baby wasn't going to make him love her.

'If you want me to believe you're not having an affair with Margot, you'll tell me what you talked about yesterday afternoon,' she said, and saw his face harden.

'I already told you no.'

The pain of it overrode everything else. 'Then you can go to bed on your own!' she snapped.

'A promise is a promise,' he reminded her sardonically. 'We're going to do everything in our power to fulfil it. Who knows, pregnancy might even mature you a little.'

He leaned down and took hold of her by the shoulders when she failed to move, drawing her to her feet. 'Either you come willingly, or I'll sling you over my shoulder and carry you up,' he threatened.

Caryn believed him. Stirred by a sudden and undeniable flutter of excitement, she was even tempted for a moment to make him do it. The moment passed. From the expression on his face, he was dangerously close to losing his temper with her completely. She wasn't prepared to risk that.

Logan recognised her capitulation with a twist of his lips. 'Very wise,' he said. 'I'm in no mood for game-playing.'

'It's no game to me either,' she denied. 'There's such a thing as marital rape.'

'And you're saying that's what I'll have to do to you?' There was a hard amusement in his voice. 'We'll see, shall we?'

They went upstairs together in person but further apart in spirit than they had ever been. Difficult though it might be to stay aloof from Logan's lovemaking, she would do it, Caryn vowed. She would lie there like a log, just to show him!

Show him what exactly? came the sudden deflating question. That she really was as immature as he believed her to be? She had spent the whole of the past week in contention with him—or most of it—and where had it got her? If he had sought a real woman's company by way of relief, then she was herself partly to blame.

He began undressing as soon as they were in the bedroom, leaving her to do the same. She took the bathroom first because she was ready first, turning on the shower and stripping off her wrap again to step into the roomy cabinet.

The rushing warm water brought a certain uplift in spirits. Something to do with negative ions, she believed. No matter how far from ideal Logan's reasons for marrying her had been, they *were* married and it was time to start trying to make a go of it. First of all she had to believe him about Margot, even if he continued to refuse to say why he had arranged to meet her. At the same time, *he* had to believe *her* when she denied any interest at all in Tod Garfield. Logan himself was the only man who could arouse any sensuality in her. She had to convince him of that.

Engrossed in her thoughts, she was unaware of the cabinet door opening, only realising when Logan slid both arms about her to draw her close up against his naked body.

'I want you,' he said roughly. He ran the tip of his tongue up behind her ear, drawing an immediate and heart-jerking response. 'I can't stop wanting you!'

He turned her about to kiss her with a passion that was close to anger, moulding her to him with hands that left her no escape. Not that she wanted to escape. Her shower cap slipped off, baring her head to the gushing water. She didn't care about that either. The only thing she did care about right now was the feel of the hard male body against hers, the swift flooding tide of desire.

When he lifted her up she knew neither reticence nor uncertainty, sliding both legs about his waist to join with him in a union she was not only ready for but positively desperate for, kissing him back with a fervency that drove him beyond all control; whispering nameless things against his lips as sheer soaring pleasure overwhelmed her.

She was weak and trembling when he finally lowered her back to the shower floor again, burying her face in his chest in sudden realisation of her own abandonment. She had never imagined doing anything like that—hadn't even considered any other way of making love but the obvious. It had been out of this world, but she couldn't bring herself to look at him.

The water was still running. Logan reached out and turned it off, but made no move to put her from him, caressing her back with slow and gentle strokes.

'You just gave me the most pleasure I ever had in my life,' he said softly against her wet hair. 'Do you know that?'

'I...don't know what to say,' Caryn whispered without lifting her head, and he laughed.

'You could try telling me how you liked it yourself.'

Like was hardly an adequate word to describe her sensations, she thought, but which one would be? 'Very much,' she murmured with restraint.

He held her a little away from him to look into her face, smiling at the sudden flush of colour under her skin. 'There's nothing to be shy about in making love, whichever way it's expressed. You followed your instincts, that's all—the same way you did the other night.' He kissed her gently on the lips. 'Better dry your hair before bed.'

He got out of the cabinet first and reached for one of the big thick bathtowels, wrapped it about her as she emerged, then took another for himself. Caryn seized a smaller towel for her hair and rubbed at it vigorously. She felt radiant, exultant—ready for anything. Perhaps they would make love again before sleeping. She wanted to; how much she wanted to! The more pleasure she could give Logan, the less likely he was to seek it elsewhere.

He insisted she dry her hair thoroughly with a hair-dryer before getting into bed, lying there watching her with a smile on his lips. Caryn switched off the bedside light before shedding her wrap to slide in beside him, eager for the warm strength of his arms.

His kiss held a tenderness that moved her to new depths of feeling for him. She loved him so much, so very, very much, this wonderful, masterful man of hers! From now on she was going to be all he could ever need in a woman. What she didn't know, he could teach her.

'Show me what you want me to do,' she whispered. 'Anything and everything!'

He didn't respond the way she expected him to, but just continued to hold her, his lips moving to her temple. 'There's more to it than simple acrobatics,' he said on a suddenly wry note. 'Just as there's more to marriage than sex alone.'

She lay still and silent, aware of having disappointed him in some way. So what had he expected from her? she asked herself achingly—a declaration of undying love? She would only do that if and when he was ready to reciprocate, not before. She had her pride too.

Duncan arrived at six-thirty and spent fifteen minutes chatting with Helen before he and Caryn left for Norwich. Logan was down at the stables still. She hadn't seen him since lunchtime.

'It was very sensible of you to agree to this,' Duncan remarked in the car. 'We're living in a lousy age when women are at such risk, but that's the way it is. I was concerned for you on Wednesday—especially after Logan rang to ask what time you left. It was a real relief when he rang back to say you'd arrived home safely.' He gave her a sideways glance, a smile touching his lips. 'You're not too enthused about it, are you?'

'No,' Caryn admitted. 'Although I'm grateful, of course, for the thought. It's just... well, do you worry about Margot the same way?'

The smile altered character. 'Margot's a different matter. She goes her own way regardless. She always did.'

'Did you know that when you married her?' The words were out before Caryn really thought about it, horrifying her with their effrontery. 'I'm sorry,' she tagged on quickly. 'That's none of my business.'

His shrug dismissed the apology. 'It's common knowledge that we're undergoing difficulties. The marriage was a mistake to begin with—from both sides. My first wife was the complete antithesis. She died of the same thing Helen is suffering from.'

Caryn gave him a swift glance. 'I didn't know anyone else knew about it.'

'I recognise the signs. And you just confirmed it.' He shook his head as she made a sound of distress. 'I shan't spread it around. Anne felt the same way about other people knowing.'

'I'm so sorry.' Caryn could think of nothing else to say.

'One of those things no one can do anything about, I'm afraid. We had three wonderful years together. That's more than a lot can claim. You remind me of her in some ways. She was only nineteen when we married.'

'You couldn't have been so much older.'

'I was twenty-five, but it isn't the number of years between that matters, it's what you feel for a person. Logan's a fine man. It's only natural for him to be concerned for your wellbeing. Don't repudiate it for the sake of a little feminine independence.'

Would he regard Logan as such a fine man if he knew about yesterday's meeting? Caryn wondered. Regardless of any marital problems, Margot was still his wife. Whatever had taken place—or not taken place—the assignation itself was wrong to start with.

'I'll try not to,' she said, keeping a tight rein on the rest. There was more to most relationships than met the eye; she was only just beginning to appreciate that fact.

They did little that evening apart from reading through the script. A romantic comedy, the play had some very funny lines and situations, and a tender love story too. Caryn could identify with the young heroine in love with an older man, although the age gap was actually some years less than her own. Their story finished happily. She could only hope and trust that hers and Logan's would eventually work out the same.

Tod was over-attentive, and not averse to criticising
Logan for what he termed the latter's 'heavy father' attitude when he learned of the arrangement with Duncan.

'You're surely not going to let him dictate your every
move, are you?' he said on a belittling note. 'I thought
you had more spirit than that!'

'Duncan made the offer,' she defended. 'I could hardly
throw it in his face.'

'They're two of a kind, and always have been. I never
could understand what it was that Margot saw in either
of them, to be honest. She's hardly the submissive type.'

Neither was she, if it came to that, thought Caryn,
but it hadn't stopped her from falling for Logan. Margot
wouldn't have given way on such an issue for certain.
But then Margot was obviously well able to look after
herself.

'You know she and Duncan are splitting up?' Tod
asked now, watching her expression.

'It isn't any business of mine,' Caryn replied sharply,
and saw his lips slant.

'It might be if she's still carrying a torch for that
husband of yours. What our Margot wants, she goes all
out for.'

'It takes two,' she retorted with a tartness that was
pure cover.

'Every time,' he agreed. 'You know what they say
about——'

'If you've finished your coffee, we may as well make
tracks,' said Duncan, causing Caryn to start because she
hadn't seen him approaching.

It was difficult to tell from his expression whether he
had overheard anything—although she doubted if he
would show any response if he had. Tod was right about
he and Logan being alike in many ways.

'I'm ready,' she said.

Avril was looking resigned again. Caryn attempted to convey assurance in her smile, but doubted if she succeeded in getting her lack of interest in Tod's attentions across. The next time he made any attempt to single her out, she would tell him straight to leave her alone, she promised herself.

It would have been simple enough to repeat that decision when Duncan suggested more or less the same thing on the way back to Whitegates, but at the time she was conscious only of resentment over what she took to be criticism of her own behaviour. There was every chance that Logan had asked for an eye to be kept on her, she fumed. Two-faced, to say the least, when he was meeting this same man's wife in secret—whatever the reason!

'I don't have any cause to keep Tod Garfield at a distance,' she returned with forced politeness. 'There's no harm in talking to someone, is there?'

'That isn't the kind of distance I'm talking about,' came the level reply. 'Women find Tod very attractive, and he tends to take advantage of it.'

'Only if they allow it. I'm quite capable of handling any advances, thanks.'

'Fair enough.' Duncan's tone was mild. 'Just so long as you know.'

Warning given, job done for the moment, but the eye would still be kept on her, Caryn was certain. Both Logan and now Duncan, it seemed, believed her incapable of resisting Tod's blandishments. A mild flirtation on Monday evening was surely no cause to suspect her whole moral fibre?

The subject was shelved after that, but the damage was done. Caryn could feel the anger and hurt simmering inside her, ready to come to the boil at the least excuse. No matter how little Logan might trust her

judgement, he had no right to bring Duncan into it. One
thing was certain, she would *not* be dictated to!

She made no effort to invite Duncan in when they
reached the house. It was even on the tip of her tongue
to tell him she wouldn't be attending any further rehearsals, but she bit it back. Logan would be only too
pleased to have her out of Tod's reach, and she wasn't
going to give him that satisfaction. If he wouldn't tell
her the reason he'd met with Margot the other afternoon,
why should she put his mind at rest over Tod Garfield?
Let him think what he liked. Let them *all* think what
they liked!

He came to the drawing-room door when she entered
the house, with every indication from the casual way he
was dressed of having spent the whole evening relaxing
at home.

'Duncan not coming in?' he asked. 'I've got a fresh
pot of coffee waiting.'

'We already had coffee,' Caryn replied shortly. 'I
suppose he thought it a bit late for visiting.' She added
with deliberation, 'After all, Margot would be wondering where he'd got to.'

Logan's smile was fleeting. 'No doubt. So, how did
it go?'

'Fine. I'm to be prompt.' She had no conscious intention of making mischief, but the words seemed to say
themselves. 'Tod Garfield is taking the male lead, of
course. He's a natural for the part.'

'I'm sure.' The grey eyes had narrowed a little. 'Did
you want any more coffee yourself?'

Caryn shook her head, already regretting the in-
nuendo. It was bad enough having Logan suspect her of
being interested in Tod at all without adding conviction
by mentioning his name within a couple of minutes of
arriving home. Why didn't she just tell him the truth?

She didn't because those particular words were held back by some stronger force. Why should she be the only one to suffer jealousy—if that was what he was feeling. Logan might not love her, but he considered her wholly his. Possession was only nine points of the law. He should be made aware of that.

'I think I'll go straight to bed,' she said. 'I'm rather tired.'

It was only just eleven, but he revealed no scepticism. 'I'll be up shortly,' he said, and she wondered if it was only her imagination that made the statement sound vaguely threatening.

She lay awake for what seemed an age before he finally came up. The anger and resentment had given way by then to a more desperate emotion, swathing heart and mind with the need to feel his arms about her, his body joined with hers. No matter how he felt or didn't feel about her, she couldn't live without his love-making. Not now.

He made no attempt to take hold of her when he slid into bed, but simply lay there on his back. After five long minutes, unable to stand the suspense any longer, Caryn rolled over towards him, sliding her arms about his neck to press her lips to the strong column of his throat, reaching for him with a wantonness she would never have dared to express a bare week ago.

Regardless of his forbearance, he was already aroused, she found. He made a guttural sound beneath his breath and seized her about the waist, bringing her over on top of him and fitting her to him, holding her upright with his hands at her breasts as they came wholly and wonderfully together. His eyes glittered up at her in the moonlight.

'Anything and everything—wasn't that what you said?' he asked softly.

Later—much later—lying spent in his arms, Caryn
found time to wonder at her temerity during the last hour
or so. She had not only followed where he led, but taken
initiatives of her own, driven by an overriding need to
prove herself a match for any other woman he had ever
known—including Margot. For a man like Logan, lovemaking in itself was an essential part of life, but for her
it was only the one man who could make her feel the
same way. The only thing she wouldn't do to keep him
was share him with anyone else.

'I think,' he murmured, 'that I'm going to need plenty
of stamina to deal with you, my darling.'

'Are you complaining?' she queried softly, and heard
his low laugh.

'Show me the man who would!' He kissed her temple
where the hair clung damply, lips heartwarmingly tender.
'Go to sleep. There's always tomorrow.'

And many more after it, Caryn hoped. She could make
this marriage of theirs work out—she *would* make it
work out. The gap was already narrowing.

Woken for the first time by a kiss, she found morning
lovemaking equally enjoyable. Logan stirred himself with
reluctance to get out of bed at seven-thirty, leaving her
to watch him through slitted eyelids as he gathered his
things to take into the bathroom. Her face felt slightly
tender where the bristle along his jawline had rubbed it,
but she had no quarrel with that. There was a lovely
intimacy about kissing a man in need of a shave.

She loved him so much! she thought achingly. Last
night's rancour seemed of little importance right now.

If Helen was surprised to see the two of them at
breakfast together, she didn't show it. She looked more
rested this morning, Caryn reflected, and wondered if it
were possible that she might be achieving a further remission after all. If she did it would mean Logan's future

plans would have to be amended, of course, but he would hardly begrudge his mother a little more time.

'Will you have time to give me another riding lesson today?' she asked him before they left the table.

'This afternoon,' he said. 'This morning we'll take a trip into Norwich and get you properly kitted out.' He added to his mother, 'Do you feel up to coming with us?'

Helen smiled and shook her head. 'I've one or two letters to write. Why don't you have lunch in town while you're at it? There'll still be plenty of time for riding when you get back.'

'Good idea,' he agreed easily. 'Is Joplin's still going, do you know?'

'I believe so,' she said. 'If it isn't, there are plenty of other places to eat.'

Caryn didn't care where they went. Spending the whole day with Logan would be a bonus in itself. Perhaps on the way back they might find time to call in on her parents too. The more they saw of their son-in-law, the sooner they would come round to accepting him.

It turned out even better than she had anticipated. Not only did she acquire a whole riding wardrobe, but Logan also suggested that she take the opportunity to replenish her general wardrobe, while they were at it. Caryn was happy to ask his opinion, finishing up with several new outfits of a quality and design she would never have been able to afford out of her own pocket.

'It's cost an absolute fortune!' she exclaimed over lunch, doing a mental calculation. 'You'll have to take it out of my allowance, of course—providing there's enough.'

'I doubt if there'll be any problem.' Logan sounded amused. 'When are you going to stop worrying about money?'

'It's going to take time,' she acknowledged. 'I'm just not used to spending quite so freely.' Her laugh was light-hearted. 'Not that I'm complaining, of course! Who would?'

The grey eyes appraised the thickly layered blonde hair and finely boned young face, dwelling for a moment or two on the fullness of her mouth. 'Not me,' he said softly.

Her breath caught in her throat as emotion swamped her. She gazed back at him with her heart in her eyes— or so she imagined. He had to know how much she loved him. He couldn't fail to know. If only she could make him feel the same way for her!

'Keep looking at me like that,' he growled, low-toned, 'and I'm going to need a cold shower before I dare stand up!'

'I don't care,' she said recklessly. 'I want you!'

His smile was dry. 'Right attitude, wrong venue. Try exercising a little discretion.'

He hadn't meant that seriously, Caryn assured herself as he signalled the waiter for the bill. No one else could have overheard. She only wished she had the courage to say what she really wanted to say to him.

CHAPTER TEN

THEY were in the car heading back to Whitegates when Logan said casually, 'How do you feel about going to the Country Club tonight? It's the monthly dinner dance.'

'Who else is likely to be there?' Caryn asked, torn between wanting to have him to herself and the knowledge that he probably needed other company by way of a change.'

'Oh, the usual crowd, I suppose. Many of them you already met.'

Including Margot? she wondered. She made an effort to put the thought aside; there was no use dwelling on something Logan had more or less sworn hadn't happened. Trust me, he had said, so she would—or certainly try to.

'Yes, I'd like to,' she agreed. 'Providing your mother doesn't mind being left on her own for the evening.'

He shook his head. 'The last thing she'd want is for the two of us to hang around all the time. That would only make her feel worse. She mentioned a film on television she wanted to see, so she'll probably welcome the opportunity. We'll not be leaving before eight, anyway.'

He seemed to have it all arranged already, Caryn reflected, which seemed to indicate that her agreement had been taken for granted. But then he would have had to reserve a table in advance, wouldn't he? Reservations could always be cancelled should plans fall through.

There was no attempt on Logan's part to delay the promised ride. Clad in her new jodhpurs and shining

165

brown boots, Caryn felt like a true rider. Logan rode Ballantyne, and kept Dorea on the leading rein for the first ten minutes or so until convinced that Caryn could handle her.

They stayed on Bannister land, but covered a fair distance, walking their mounts for the most part, although Caryn was eager to try out a canter or two.

'A couple of weeks of this and you'll be ready for the show ring,' Logan joked, reining in under the lee of the hedge in the bottom meadow to tighten a girth. 'You've taken to horseback like a duck to water!'

'Swan would be more complimentary,' Caryn responded in mock indignation, and he laughed.

'Ducks are very appealing creatures, but swan it is. Anything to keep you happy.'

'I am,' she said impulsively. 'Very happy!'

Logan straightened to look at her, eyes crinkling at the corners. 'Any particular reason?'

The words trembled on her lips, but still refused to emerge. 'Who wouldn't be happy on a day like this, doing what we're doing?' she prevaricated. 'I never realised what I was missing!'

'No, of course you didn't.' The smile still lingered on his lips, though somehow altered in character. 'Sorry to spoil the idyll, but I think you've done enough for today. You're using a set of muscles you haven't used before. As it is, you're going to ache tomorrow.'

Caryn made no protest as he started Ballantyne moving towards the gate. His mood had changed, and she didn't know why. Boredom, probably. It had to be frustrating taking out a total novice when he was accustomed to riding free.

Helen gave no indication of anything but pleasure at the news that they were going to be out for the evening. It was, she said, high time they began circulating. The re-run of *Casablanca* would keep her fully entertained, she assured Caryn. Humphrey Bogart had always been a favourite of hers.

The dinner dances were only full evening dress on special occasions, Logan advised when asked what to wear. One of the things they had bought that morning would be perfectly suitable. With what he had said on the previous occasion in mind, Caryn put on a chocolate-brown dress with a scooped out neckline and a swirly skirt that ended inches above her knees. Her pearls looked good with it, as did the ivory shoes and handbag from Marcelle. Altogether different from last Monday's appearance.

'That's more your style,' Logan agreed. 'Utterly delectable, in fact,' he added lightly.

He was looking more than palatable himself in the beautifully tailored pale grey trousers and darker jacket, Caryn reflected, feeling her senses stir as she glanced at him. He wore clothes so well.

Her husband. It might not be a perfect marriage, but it was a real one. Here or in Australia, they were going to stay together. She was determined on that.

They hadn't called on her parents after all, she recalled on the way out to the club. She had seen them only the once herself since returning from honeymoon, and Logan not at all. That matter would have to be rectified, and soon. Perhaps tomorrow. Sunday was a good day for visiting.

Obviously exclusive, the club was set in its own spacious grounds. There were tennis courts, an indoor swimming pool and a gymnasium for the health conscious, plus a fine bar and restaurant for those more indulgently inclined.

The former was already well populated. Once again, Caryn found herself the youngest person present, but it no longer bothered her as much. With Logan to support her, she could hold her own with this crowd—or any other, for that matter.

Tonight even Margot failed to put too great a dent in her self-esteem, beautiful though the other looked in a ruby-coloured dress that was as short as Caryn's own. At twenty-seven, she was still well within Logan's stated demarcation line, and her legs were certainly good enough, but he appeared to spare her no more attention than the rest of the women. Standing at his side, arm brushing his sleeve, Caryn felt a swelling sense of well-being.

Dinner was excellent, the four-piece combo equally so. Several groups shared tables pushed together. Asked to join Duncan's party, Logan made no objection, although Caryn would have preferred to stay where they were. An unsocial inclination, she chided herself. No two people could, or even should, spend all their time on their own.

Dancing with him for the first time was a dream. He held her close enough for her to feel the beat of his heart, to relish the lithe movement of thigh muscle. The extra height gained from the heels she was wearing brought her eyes level with his mouth—that firm, decisive, utterly devastating mouth that had given her so much pleasure in nights past, and would again in the night to come, she trusted. Feeling the way she did, she could weather anything but losing him. He was her whole life!

He danced with the other women in the party too, of course. Caryn only minded when it came to Margot's turn to be asked, try as she might to ignore the pang. She also did her best not to watch the pair of them as they moved around the floor, but it was a losing battle. They seemed to be talking so intimately, looking into each other's eyes in a way that roused new suspicions in her heart.

Avril Garfield was dancing with one of the other men in the party, leaving Tod sitting out. He got up and came round the tables to where Caryn was seated, smiling down at her with accomplished charm.

'As Duncan and Co. seem preoccupied with business matters, and your husband and my wife are otherwise engaged, perhaps you'll give me a dance?'

About to refuse, Caryn caught another glimpse of the two dark heads so close together, the arms entwined about Logan's neck, and abruptly changed her mind. Logan would only hold a woman that way if he wanted to.

'I thought you'd never ask!' she exclaimed with overdone vivacity.

Tod looked a little surprised at the sudden new warmth, but gratified too. His ego needed little boosting. He drew her close as soon as they took to the floor.

'You make all the other women here tonight look like grandmothers!' he murmured into her hair. 'Have you any idea what you do to me?'

Held this close, Caryn had a very good idea, and didn't care for it. She eased herself away a little, resisting the urge to knee him in the groin. It was her own fault she was here with him—her own fault if he had the wrong idea regarding her motives. Paying Logan back in his own coin didn't seem such a good idea right now.

'Don't tease,' Tod admonished. 'You did enough of that Monday night.' His laugh was low. 'You really had me convinced with that little-girl-lost act!'

'It wasn't an act,' she denied, relinquishing her pose. 'I didn't like what you tried then, and I don't like it now! Why can't you just be friendly, like Duncan?'

'Because you're not built for it,' he said. 'And don't take it for granted that I'm the only one you affect this way. Logan's the envy of every man in the place.'

If he meant that statement to flatter her, he was sadly mistaken, she reflected. All it did do was underline his total lack of finesse. She felt sorry for Avril, who must have the tolerance of a saint to put up with his philandering. That kind of marriage wasn't for her, and Logan had better realise it.

They finished the dance in near silence. Tod appeared to have got the message all right, but after this she would definitely be offering no further encouragement, Caryn vowed. Logan and Margot had already returned to their respective seats when they came off the floor. Logan's expression was unrevealing.

Murmuring an insincere thanks, Tod moved off back to his own seat. Caryn slid into hers, reaching for her wine glass with a surprisingly steady hand and swallowing the remaining contents.

'Refill?' asked one of the other men seated opposite, having just replenished his own glass.

Logan answered for her, voice easy enough on the surface but with an undertone that wasn't to be ignored. 'I think not, thanks.'

Caryn drew in a slow, uneven breath. 'I can speak for myself,' she said jerkily as the other turned away with a good-humoured shrug. 'I can also decide when I've had enough to drink!'

'No, you can't,' came the measured response. 'You're already over the limit. It's about time we made tracks, anyway.'

It was only just gone eleven, and no one else was leaving. Caryn shook her head, lying through her teeth. 'I don't want to go yet.'

'Tough.' He pushed back his chair, eyes challenging her to argue about it. 'I'll go and bring the car round to the door.'

For a fleeting moment she was tempted to defy him outright, but only for a moment. He would think nothing of packing her out bodily if it became necessary. Margot was watching the two of them with a supercilious little smile on her lips. Under no circumstances, it said, would any man tell *her* what to do. No one else appeared to have noticed the discord as yet. With little real choice, Caryn seized the line of least resistance.

Their leaving elicited some surprise all round. The evening was only just getting into its stride, it was pointed out. Logan offered no excuses, leaving one or two of the men to draw their own obvious conclusions, certified by the sly smiles. One thing they would not be doing tonight, Caryn could have told them, was making love. Not after his performance with Margot!

The journey home was accomplished in silence from both sides. As before, Logan left her to go indoors alone while he garaged the car.

Mrs Lawson had left the hall and library lights on. The latter, Caryn assumed, in case Logan might fancy a nightcap. Moved by a sudden urge to show him she still had a mind of her own, she went in and poured herself a brandy, tossing it back without even tasting it. The effects were by no means slow in making themselves felt, however. Her whole body felt energised, her mind needle-sharp and ready for battle.

She was standing there, glass in hand, when Logan came into the room. He stopped dead when he saw her, jaw compressing, then came swiftly across to snatch the glass from her.

'What the devil do you think you're doing, you little fool?' he demanded savagely.

'Seeking solace,' she said with what she believed to be amazing clarity of both thought and speech. 'Isn't that what deceived wives do?' She didn't wait for an answer, eyes sparking like twin sapphires as she faced up to him with hatred in her mind if not her heart. 'Don't try denying it. You were all over her on the dance-floor tonight!'

'On the contrary,' he clipped, '*she* was all over *me*. It's difficult to unhook a woman's arms from about one's neck without damage if she doesn't want them unhooked.'

'A likely story!' Caryn was in no way convinced. '*You* asked *her* to dance, not the other way round.'

'I danced with the other women on our table too, if you recall. It's called common courtesy.' The grey eyes held a glitter of their own. 'The same reason, I trust, that you accepted Tod Garfield's invitation.'

The need to make him seethe with jealousy the way she was seething overrode whatever caution the brandy had left her with. Her smile was pure malice. 'Oh, of course! Like you, I hated every moment of it.'

The reaction she saw in his face was like a dash of cold water in hers, although not quite cold enough to oust the sudden, alcohol-induced malaise. She put a hand to her mouth with a sound of distress as her stomach heaved, trying not to retch.

'I don't feel very well,' she got out between her fingers.

Logan swore under his breath and bent to slide an arm under her knees, lifting her up against his chest. Caryn closed her eyes as the room spun about her, keeping them closed as he carried her from the room. She had never felt like this before, and never wanted to feel like this again!

He carried her all the way up to their room, depositing her on the bed with a gentleness she knew she didn't deserve. Still feeling sick and dizzy, she could find neither will nor strength to attempt any immediate reconciliation, but simply lay there with her hand over her eyes waiting for the room to stand still.

'I'll leave you to sleep it off,' Logan said quietly, and left.

She did sleep in the end, although there were moments when she was sure she would have to rush for the bathroom. Waking still fully dressed to morning light was dismaying enough, but not nearly as much as the blinding headache that struck her between the eyes the moment she tried lifting her head from the pillow.

Moaning, she fell back flat again. If this was a hangover, then it was the very last one she would ever suffer! How did people stand it time and time again?

She had acted so stupidly last night. No matter how she felt about things, there was no excuse for that kind of behaviour. She should have faced Logan with the matter calmly and coolly, and told him it had to stop. He might have respected her for that.

She was fooling herself, and she knew it. No matter what she did, or how she acted, Logan would never see her in any other light but that of the too young bride he had been forced by circumstances to make the best of. Everything he had taught her had been for his own benefit not hers. He was a sensual man who needed a woman capable of answering his needs. She hadn't been at first, but she had learned—how she had learned! Only it wasn't enough. Not for him. A woman like Margot could supply so much more.

The opening of the door brought her head up again, and a fresh stab of pain. Logan came over to the bed carrying a glass of something foaming in his hand. He was fully dressed in jodhpurs and light sweater, and looked totally unmoved by events.

'If you're feeling anything like I imagine you're feeling, you're going to need this,' he said. 'Try sitting up a little or you're going to spill it.'

Caryn lifted herself on an elbow, wincing as the pounding at her temple increased again. Thankfully, the nausea seemed to have passed. She couldn't have coped with that too.

'What is it?' she asked thickly, taking the glass from him.

'It doesn't matter,' he said. 'Just drink it. The effects won't be immediate, but you should start feeling better in a little while. In the meantime, you'd better stay where you are.'

The bubbles had settled by now, leaving a liquid that sparkled in the shaft of sunlight striking in through the window. It tasted slightly salty, though not unpleasantly so. Caryn drained the glass and handed it back, glad to collapse into the pillows again.

'What time is it?'

'Just gone half-past seven,' Logan answered. 'I'm going for a ride, but I'll be back for breakfast.'

The very thought of eating made her stomach turn over. Avoiding direct contact with the grey eyes, she said diffidently, 'Where did you sleep last night?'

His smile was brief. 'There's no shortage of bedrooms. You were showing signs of restlessness when I came in to get dressed, so I judged you'd be about ready for a pick-me-up by now. Anyway, try and sleep again. You'll feel better for it.'

'Logan.' The name came out on a husky note as he started to turn away, drawing his gaze back to her face again. His expression hadn't altered.

'Yes?'

'I'm ... sorry,' she forced between stiff lips. 'It was a stupid thing to do.'

'Yes, it was,' he agreed. 'But it probably saved me from doing something *I'd* have regretted.' The smile came again, just as brief, just as lacking in humour. 'You're not the only one liable to lose sight of the main objective at times.'

The main objective being his mother's peace of mind, Caryn acknowledged numbly, which was hardly going to be sustained by any obvious friction between the two of them.

'Can we forget it?' she said, and saw one dark brow lift.

'*All* of it?'

He meant Margot, of course, and she wasn't prepared to go that far even for Helen's sake. If this marriage of theirs was going to stand any chance at all, then he had to put the woman aside for good.

His lips twisted when she failed to answer. 'I think we need to have a long, straight talk,' he said. 'But obviously not now. If you feel up to it, we'll go and visit your parents after lunch.'

He was gone before she could make any reply, closing the door quietly behind him.

It was ten or fifteen minutes before the headache began to ease, and another fifteen after that before Caryn could summon the will to stir herself. Her face in the mirror looked washed out, her eyes like finger holes in snow, and her hair was all over the place. Shuddering, she went to get a shower, standing under the flow of warm water until her head began to feel as if it belonged to her again.

Towelled dry, she donned fresh underwear, and blow-dried her hair, thankful for the expert styling that allowed it to fall so naturally into shape. Lipstick gave her face a much-needed lift. Dressed in trousers and long-sleeved shirt, she looked almost normal.

Breakfast on a Sunday wasn't until nine, giving
everyone—including the Lawsons—opportunity for a bit
of a lie-in if they fancied it. Caryn doubted if Logan
ever had. His energy was boundless, the day hardly long
enough to start with. If she hadn't been indisposed, he
might have suggested taking an early morning ride
together. She would have liked that so much.

Both mother and son were already at table when she
finally got down. There was no hint of anything but solicitous enquiry in the former's greeting.

'You could have had a tray brought up to you,' Helen
added. 'There's nothing like breakfast in bed after a late
night.'

Caryn forced a smile, avoiding so much as a glance
in Logan's direction. 'I'm sure Mrs Lawson has enough
to do without running about after me.'

Helen laughed. 'I was thinking more in terms of this
husband of yours doing the honours. You'd have been
only too delighted, wouldn't you, Logan?' The last with
a glint of wicked humour in the look she directed her
son's way.

'Absolutely,' he said drily.

Caryn helped herself to cereal and poured coffee from
the pot ready waiting. She still didn't feel like eating,
and even less like drinking coffee, but Helen mustn't be
allowed to guess the real cause of her tardiness. It was
enough for Logan to know. A long straight talk, he had
said, but no amount of talking was going to alter the
basic problem. They were incompatible in every way but
the one—and it wasn't enough.

She spent the morning out on the terrace with her
mother-in-law, while Logan spent his down at the stables.

'You must tell him if you feel he's neglecting you,'
advised Helen at one point. 'I know he's keen to get
things organised, but there has to be a limit on what can

be done at the weekends.' She studied the younger face opposite as if weighing something in balance. 'As one who never had anything to do with them before, you must find his interest in horses a bit too consuming at times.'

'Not now I'm learning to ride,' Caryn assured her truthfully. 'I wouldn't mind working at the stables myself sometimes, as a matter of fact, although I don't suppose Logan would be too keen on the idea.'

'On the contrary, I think he'd be delighted to know you felt that way. The Blue River stud is very much of an all-hands-to-the-mill affair still—although there'll be substantial new capital to inject, of course, once he's sold Whitegates.'

'Don't!' Caryn couldn't keep the distress from her voice. 'I can't bear to think about it.'

'You'll get used to it,' Helen assured her on a practical note. 'The same way I have. Don't ban me from talking about your future just because I'm not going to be here. Seeing Logan married has meant such a lot to me. There was a time when I believed he might never find the right woman, but he did in the end.'

Except that she isn't woman enough, Caryn reflected numbly as her mother-in-law changed the subject. Just a girl way out of her depth.

Lunch came and went. Logan waited until his mother had gone up for her rest before reiterating his suggestion that they visit Caryn's parents. Wanting to see them, though afraid of what might be perceived, she could only agree. It would at least get the afternoon over.

It was raining when they set off. A soft summer rain that scarcely wet the roof tops, but was enough to clear holiday-makers from the beaches.

'It really seemed as if the weather was going to settle down for the rest of the summer,' Caryn observed as they turned out on to the main road. 'Much more of this, and Barston won't have any season left to finish.'

'If the town wants to compete in the tourist market, then it's going to need some restructuring,' Logan answered. 'It can be done without ruining the place, providing enough care is taken. A leisure centre with facilities for rainy days like this one, for a start. I've seen ones with freeform swimming pools you'd almost swear were out of doors.'

'To be built where, and financed how?' she queried.

Broad shoulders lifted. 'Not my problem. Not yours either,' he added with deliberation. 'We might not be here this time next year.'

She said huskily, '*You* might not.'

He gave her a swift hard glance. 'Are you trying to tell me something?'

'Only that mistakes can be rectified. Once your mother...' She hesitated, swallowing on the dry ache in her throat. 'We don't have to stay married.'

'Start divorce proceedings the minute she's gone, you mean?' The tone was clipped. 'Is that what you want?'

'It might be best.'

'For whom? I don't recall giving any indication of dissatisfaction.' He shook his head, profile austere. 'Let it lie for now.'

She hadn't intended bringing the subject up, Caryn acknowledged wryly. The words had formed themselves. She wanted no divorce, but what she did want was unlikely to happen. How could she live the rest of her life with a man who didn't love her?

Her parents were surprised but not displeased to see the two of them, making Logan welcome in a way that warmed Caryn's heart. He was a past master at dissembling, sitting there so easy and relaxed; smiling at her as if nothing untoward had passed between them. It

was she who found difficulty in hiding her emotions—
a fact evidenced by her mother's somewhat tentative
query when the two of them were alone for a moment
or two in the kitchen.

'Is there anything wrong?' she said. 'You seem very
quiet.'

'Just a bit tried,' Caryn claimed. 'We went to the
Country Club last night. A dinner dance.'

'I shouldn't have thought an occasion like that so
taxing.' Susan was obviously not entirely convinced, but
equally obviously reluctant to press the issue. 'I suppose
you'll be doing a lot of socialising?'

'No more than most.' Caryn sought a change of topic.
'I've joined the Priory Players in Norwich. And I'm
learning to ride. Life's pretty full all round.'

'How is Helen?'

'The same. We'll be going out to lunch together
tomorrow. Why don't you come too? She'd be absolutely delighted if you did.'

Her mother hesitated, then shook her head. 'Another
time, perhaps.'

Caryn left it at that. It was no use trying to forge a
relationship between the two without joint enthusiasm.
She wasn't even all that certain of her mother-in-law's
likely reaction.

They left at four in order to be back at Whitegates in
good time for tea.

'I like your parents,' said Logan conversationally as
they drew away from the house. 'Given time, they may
even come to forgive me my trespasses.' He cast a glance
when Caryn made no reply. 'Incidentally, I'll be joining
the drama group after all. Duncan is a great persuader.'

'And an even greater tale-teller, I suppose!' she responded with asperity.

'Suggesting there are tales to tell?' He sounded more ironic than angry. 'I didn't ask Duncan to keep an eye on you, if that's what you're thinking. Neither am I joining the group to do the same. You've made the effort to share my interests; I'm simply returning the compliment.'

If she could believe that it would be a considerable boost, Caryn acknowledged wryly, but she didn't believe it. He didn't trust her around Tod Garfield, that was the crux of the matter. This was his way of making sure she toed the line—regardless of what he might get up to with Margot.

He said nothing more after that. There was, she supposed, nothing more to *be* said. She considered resigning from the group herself, but that would be cutting off her nose to spite her face. At least while he was attending rehearsals he couldn't be meeting Margot.

Helen was obviously pleased to see the two of them return, although she'd only been down half an hour, by her own acknowledgement, so had hardly had time to feel deserted. Her rest periods were growing slightly longer each day, Caryn realised, looking back over the week. There would come a time, she supposed, when the fatigue would be constant. Helen might have accepted the inevitability of it all, but she doubted if she ever could. It was so utterly unfair!

Logan didn't linger long over tea, announcing that he was going down to the stables. The rain had stopped over an hour ago, although the skies threatened more to come. If he planned on going riding again, the time was now, Caryn supposed, and wished he would ask her to go with him. That long, straight talk seemed suddenly imperative.

By seven o'clock, with still no sign of him, she was beginning to wonder if he intended staying out all evening. Helen herself expressed some annoyance with her son for his lack of consideration. It was, she said, inexcusable of him.

When Duncan turned up some minutes later, one look at his face was enough to tell both women that this was no social call.

'I'm afraid Logan had an accident,' he said. 'He's been taken to the Norwich. Alive,' he hastened to add, 'though unconscious. He took a knock on the head. I happened to be driving along the coast road behind the car that ran into him. Not Logan's fault. The damn fool driver was going far too fast.' He made a wry gesture. 'Anyway, I told the police I'd come straight over and fetch you to the hospital.'

Caryn stirred herself, too paralysed with shock to feel anything very much as yet. 'I'll go and fetch you a coat, Helen.'

'You go with Duncan,' said her mother-in-law unevenly. 'I'll wait here. You can telephone through as soon as you know how things are.'

Caryn didn't argue. The numbness was all pervading, her mind an absolute blank. She went with Duncan out to his car, sat through the whole journey in rigid silence, face as white as a sheet.

He drove straight to Accident and Emergency on reaching the hospital, and accompanied her inside to the reception desk, where they were informed that the patient they sought was up in X-Ray at present.

'If you'd like to take a seat over there until the duty surgeon is free to see you,' the receptionist directed with the brisk authority and detachment essential to her calling.

It was a long wait—or it seemed so to Caryn as the numbness gave way to throat-wrenching anguish. If Logan died, she would want to die too. It didn't matter any more why he'd asked her to marry him, or what he might or might not have done with Margot. She loved him whatever; it was only now that she knew just how much. When she thought about the way she had acted at times this last week, she wanted to throw up. If he saw her as little more than a recalcitrant teenager, could she blame him?

Given the chance, it would all be so different, she vowed. She could make him love her if she really put her mind to it, and not only in the physical sense. No matter how fantastic, sex was only a part of a relationship, not the be all and end all. She could live without it if she had to, but she couldn't bear never to see Logan again; never to hear his voice, his deep-throated laugh.

'Mrs Bannister?' The man standing over her was wearing a white coat and a reassuring expression. 'I'm happy to be able to tell you that your husband has a concussion but no fracture. We'd prefer to keep him overnight for observation, if you can persuade him to stay, but there should be no serious repercussions.'

Caryn closed her eyes for a moment as relief washed over her, opening them again to say with gratitude, 'Thank you! Can I see him?'

'Of course. He's in cubicle three.'

'I'll phone Helen,' said Duncan. 'You go on through.'

The curtain was drawn across cubicle three. Ushered inside by the nurse who had shown her the way, Caryn stood for a brief moment just gazing at the man lying propped on the examination bed, taking in the bloody gash at his temple and general pallor.

'Hi,' he said quietly.

Wanting to rush to him, yet somehow unable to make the move, she settled instead for a shaky smile and an equally unsteady, 'Thank heaven you're all right!'

His jaw contracted. 'Ballantyne took the brunt of it. He was killed outright.'

'How do you know that if you were unconscious?' was all she could think of to say.

'Stunned, not out altogether. If I ever get my hands on that driver...'

'What happened exactly?' Caryn interrupted. 'We heard the car ran into you.'

'So it did. Doing around sixty on a forty stretch, to judge from the screech as he came round the bend and saw us in the roadside. We'd just come off the beach track.' He stopped there, wincing involuntarily as he shook his head. 'No point in going over it. Find me my boots and we'll get out of here.'

'They want you to stay overnight,' she said. 'Just for observation.'

'No way.' His tone brooked no argument. 'I'm OK.' He sat up straight and swung his legs over the edge of the bed. 'Just tell them I want my boots, will you?'

'They're here.' Caryn picked the pair of them up from the foot of the bed and brought them to him, recognising the futility in further protest. 'Duncan is outside,' she added, watching him pull the scratched and dusty riding boots back on, and noting the rip in the leg of his jodhpurs. 'He was practically on the spot when the accident happened, so he took it on himself to come and break the news rather than have the police do it. He already let your mother know you're all right.'

'Good of him. We'll get a taxi back, and save him a double journey.'

'I gather you're not staying?' said the duty surgeon, coming into the cubicle in time to hear the last.

'Save the beds for those who might need them more,' Logan advised. 'All *I* need is an aspirin or two.' He stood up, gave the other man a brief smile. 'Thanks for all the care and attention, anyway. I wouldn't have your job for a pension!'

'There are times,' came the dry return, 'when I feel that way myself. If you have any dizziness at all, call your GP.'

'Will do.' To Caryn, he added briskly, 'Let's go.'

Duncan looked somewhat taken aback to see the pair of them approaching, and more than a little indignant at the mention of a taxi.

'There's no question of it!' he declared. 'I'll run you home myself, of course.'

'You've done enough,' Logan insisted. 'More than enough. It's almost nine now. Margot will be wondering what happened to you.'

'Margot isn't home.' The tone was unrevealing. 'I'm in no hurry.'

It was Caryn who clinched the matter, voice sharply decisive. 'If Duncan is willing to take us home, then that's the way we're going to go!'

Dark brows lifted, and a smile pulled faintly at the corners of Logan's mouth. 'Is that a fact?'

'Yes, it is!' She was too angry to consider Duncan's presence. 'You can take the big strong male theme too far. If the medical profession consider that bump on the head worth concern, then the sooner you're home and able to rest, the better. We might be ages getting a taxi.'

'She's quite right.' Duncan sounded amused. 'So you don't have very much choice.'

'So it seems.' Logan sounded more than a little amused himself. 'You'd better lead on, then.'

Caryn fell into step at his side as Duncan moved ahead towards the outer doors, still too worked up to see any humour in the situation. She felt more like crying. Delayed shock, she told herself—plus her failure to say all she had wanted to say back there in the cubicle.

Logan slid an arm about her shoulders. 'You're shaking like a leaf,' he observed. 'What is it, Caryn?'

'What do you think?' she asked thickly. 'For all I knew, you could have been dead by the time we got here!'

'But I wasn't,' he said. 'All I have is a slight concussion.'

'Which you won't take seriously.'

'Will it make you any happier if I do?'

'No, because you've no intention. You'd have to be on the verge of collapse before you'd even consider calling in your GP!'

They were outside in the late evening sunlight now. Duncan waved for them to stay where they were while he went to fetch the car from the public parking area across the way. Caryn kept her eyes fixed on him, heart too full for further speech. The arm about her shoulders tightened; she felt Logan's lips at her temple.

'I didn't realise how concerned you were,' he said softly. 'Darling, I'm fine. Really I am. I'll prove it to you when we're home.'

'Your own inimitable way?' Her voice cracked. 'Do you think that's all I care about!'

It was a moment before he answered. When he did it was on a level note. 'I believe it means a great deal to you, yes. Nothing wrong in that. It means a great deal to me too. *You* mean a great deal to me.'

'Of course I do. I enabled you to fulfil the terms of your father's will.'

'That might have been the main reason I asked you to marry me, but it wasn't the only one.'

'I know. You still wanted me.' Her tone was flat now. 'I suppose I should be thankful for that much. It's not your fault that I'm lacking in other ways.'

'What other ways?' Logan spoke quietly but with a curious inflection.

'Maturity, for one. You need somebody nearer your own level. Somebody you can look on as a proper partner instead of an aggravation.'

'Is that how you see yourself?'

'It's how I've made *you* see me. I haven't acted in a very adult fashion since I found out about the will.'

'Better than I might have expected under the circumstances. I should have been honest with you in the first place. We'll save the rest until we get home,' Logan added as Duncan drew up in the car. 'We've a whole lot to sort out.'

Caryn expected him to get in the front passenger seat after putting her into the rear, but he slid in beside her instead, arm going about her again. He had to know how she felt about him, she thought hollowly, and was making every effort to be benevolent about it. She hoped he wouldn't try to make out that what he felt for her was anything but what it really was. She could live with what she already had of him, but not with pretence.

The journey seemed to take far less time than it had coming. What small talk there was came mostly from Duncan. He declined to come in when they finally reached the house.

'All being well, I'll see you both next Wednesday,' he said. 'This doesn't let you off the hook, Logan.' He waved a hand in farewell. 'Take care.'

Helen was in the drawing-room. Her relief at seeing her son walk in unaided was tempered by concern for his injury.

'You should have done what they wanted you to do and stayed overnight,' she chided. 'You never know with a head wound.'

'I'm all right,' Logan assured her. 'I'll settle for an early night.' He looked at Caryn with a smile. 'We both will.'

'You should rest,' Helen remonstrated.

'He's going to,' Caryn answered before he could open his mouth. 'Tomorrow too.'

'We'll see what tomorrow brings,' came the non-committal reply.

Caryn forced a lighter mood as they went upstairs, thinking how it might have been. Apart from the three stitches in his head, and some bruising he had yet to acknowledge, Logan had escaped unscathed from an accident that could have killed him the way it had killed his horse. He wasn't showing it, but that loss alone must be reckoning.

'I think you should go straight to bed,' she said when they reached the bedroom. 'A good night's sleep can't do any harm.'

'Neither can this,' he said purposefully, and took her in his arms to kiss her with a depth of emotion she had never known in him before, invoking an instant and unconditional response.

'You're the best thing that ever happened to me,' he claimed on a roughened note some untold time later, holding her close. 'That very first time I saw you two years ago I was sunk! I tried to stay away from you then, but I couldn't. What I did do to you was shameful.'

'No, it wasn't,' Caryn denied. 'It was wonderful! At least, it was while it lasted.' Her breath caught on the memory. 'I hated you for two whole years, but I got over it as soon as I saw you again. I couldn't help it. You were the only man I'd ever wanted to be with. You are still.'

Logan's breath was warm on her cheek, his hand tender at her breast. 'I thought I'd managed to put it all aside until I met you on the beach that first night back and realised I'd been kidding myself. You were in

my blood. I wanted to keep you there. That condition
my father made gave me all the excuse I needed.'

'But you weren't in love with me then,' Caryn said
softly, and sensed his smile.

'I might not have recognised it as such at the time,
but it was there right enough, although I was convinced
your feelings for me were purely physical. I couldn't bear
the thought of any other man so much as touching you—
hence the reaction when I saw you come in from the
terrace at the Ashleys with Tod Garfield at your back
looking so smug. Then again on Wednesday evening
when you were so late coming home...'

'And I made things even worse by acting the way I
did,' she finished for him as he broke off with a wry
shake of his head. 'You had every right to be angry. I
was an absolute brat! I ruined our wedding-night with
the same stupidity.'

'It wasn't stupidity. You were entitled to make me
suffer a little.' He gave a low, rueful laugh. 'The understatement of the year! I intended telling you the truth
some time, but only after I felt we were close enough to
put it into perspective. It hadn't occurred to me that
Margot might know about it.'

Caryn said softly, 'Was there really no chance that
you might have married her if you hadn't gone to
Australia?'

'Not a one.' Logan kissed her again, running a possessive hand over the slender curve of her hip. 'While
we're setting the record straight, I was unfair to you too
over that meeting I had with her in Thetford. She asked
to see me because she needed someone to talk to—or so
she said. I went because I felt I owed her that much for
old times' sake. In brief, she made me an offer I was
well able to resist, and I made sure she knew it. Not that

it stopped her from trying to make trouble between us, as per last night.'

'She's very good-looking,' Caryn observed, trying to be objective about it. 'I shouldn't imagine she's used to being turned down.'

'There's a first time for everything.' Logan didn't sound concerned. 'Forget about Margot. She can't hold a candle to you.' His voice roughened. 'It was wrong of me to take advantage of your feelings towards me the way I did, but I can't regret it. I love you, my darling. More than I ever thought possible.'

'I feel the same way,' she said huskily.

'Not yet,' he answered with assertion. 'But you will. I'll make sure of it.'

MILLS & BOON

Christmas Treasures

Unwrap the romance this Christmas

Four exciting new Romances by favourite Mills & Boon authors especially for you this Christmas.

A Christmas Wish -	Betty Neels
Always Christmas -	Eva Rutland
Reform Of The Rake -	Catherine George
Christmas Masquerade -	Debbie Macomber

Published: November 1994

Available from WH Smith, John Menzies, Volume One, Forbuoys, Martins, Woolworths, Tesco, Asda, Safeway and other paperback stockists.

SPECIAL PRICE : £5.70
(4 BOOKS FOR THE PRICE OF 3)

Cruel Legacy

One man's untimely death deprives a wife of her husband, robs a man of his job and offers someone else the chance of a lifetime...

Suicide — the only way out for Andrew Ryecart, facing crippling debt. An end to his troubles, but for those he leaves behind the problems are just beginning, as the repercussions of this most desperate of acts reach out and touch the lives of six different people — changing them forever.

Special large-format paperback edition

OCTOBER
£8.99

W🌐RLDWIDE

Next Month's Romances

Each month you can choose from a wide variety of romance with Mills & Boon. Below are the new titles to look out for next month, why not ask either Mills & Boon Reader Service or your Newsagent to reserve you a copy of the titles you want to buy – just tick the titles you would like and either post to Reader Service or take it to any Newsagent and ask them to order your books.

Please save me the following titles: Please tick

		✓
A VERY STYLISH AFFAIR	*Emma Darcy*	
ELEMENT OF RISK	*Robyn Donald*	
TO HAVE AND TO HOLD	*Sally Wentworth*	
BURDEN OF INNOCENCE	*Patricia Wilson*	
LOVERS NOT FRIENDS	*Helen Brooks*	
THREADS OF DESTINY	*Sara Wood*	
INNOCENT DECEIVER	*Lilian Peake*	
WHISPER OF SCANDAL	*Kathryn Ross*	
CALYPSO'S ENCHANTMENT	*Kate Walker*	
SAVING THE DEVIL	*Sophie Weston*	
BETWEEN TWO LOVES	*Rosemary Hammond*	
DREAM MAN	*Quinn Wilder*	
STEP IN THE DARK	*Marjorie Lewty*	
LOVESTORM	*Jennifer Taylor*	
DECEPTIVE DESIRE	*Sally Carr*	
A PASSIONATE DECEIT	*Kate Proctor*	

If you would like to order these books in addition to your regular subscription from Mills & Boon Reader Service please send £1.90 per title to: Mills & Boon Reader Service, Freepost, P.O. Box 236, Croydon, Surrey, CR9 9EL, quote your Subscriber No:.................................... (if applicable) and complete the name and address details below. Alternatively, these books are available from many local Newsagents including W H Smith, J Menzies, Martins and other paperback stockists from 9 December 1994.

Name:...

Address:...

....Post Code:..........................

To Retailer: If you would like to stock M&B books please contact your regular book/magazine wholesaler for details.

You may be mailed with offers from other reputable companies as a result of this application. If you would rather not take advantage of these opportunities please tick box. ☐